MAXIMA AND MINIMA

RAGNAR FRISCH

MAXIMA AND MINIMA

THEORY AND ECONOMIC APPLICATIONS

IN COLLABORATION WITH

A. NATAF

D. REIDEL PUBLISHING COMPANY / DORDRECHT-HOLLAND

RAND McNALLY & COMPANY / CHICAGO

MAXIMA ET MINIMA

Théorie et applications économiques

Dunod, Paris, 1960

Translated from the French by Express Translation Service, London

SOLE DISTRIBUTORS FOR U.S.A. AND CANADA

RAND McNALLY & COMPANY, CHICAGO

1966

Printed in The Netherlands by D. Reidel, Dordrecht

PREFACE TO THE ENGLISH EDITION

It is always difficult to be simple without becoming over-simple when one expounds a difficult subject, and I know of no field more deserving that description than econometrics. Here we are concerned with applying mathematical methods to the solution of economic and statistical problems. By their very nature, and especially because the formulae occurring in this type of problems contain a very large number of variables, these problems often involve mathematical ideas and techniques *of a relatively advanced type*, unfamiliar in general to those who might be most naturally interested in studies of this kind.

I have attempted to resolve this contradiction – which seems unsurmountable at first sight – in the following way: When I have had to approach a problem requiring the use of ideas of a more advanced level than that of college mathematics, I have started with a detailed discussion of a few particularly simple *special cases*. But I have not applied to these simple cases the elementary and easy method which might have been sufficient to solve the problem in these particular cases. On the contrary, I have applied to these simple cases the more elaborate method suitable for dealing with the general case. In this way, the reader is brought – in a quite *intuitive manner*, usually without the aid of any proof – to understand the steps leading to the generalisation. This generalisation then becomes almost evident. Experience has shown that proceeding in this way one is able to get astonishingly far with a very moderate mathematical apparatus, and to reach an understanding of the situation which is sufficient for practical needs.

This is the spirit in which the present exposition of the *Theory of Maxima and Minima* was conceived.

Maximum and minimum problems of the type that occurs in linear and non-linear and even non-convex programming have not been attacked in an extensive way in the present book. Their peculiarity is that the variables are constrained by *inequalities*, expressed by upper and lower bounds. In this case the gradient on the boundary of the admissible domain changes *discontinuously* at certain points, which makes the method of Lagrange multipliers – so convenient in other circumstances – of limited applicability, at least in its straightforward and simple form. Various aspects of the programming type of maximum and minimum problems are discussed in a number of memoranda and studies published in recent years by the University of Oslo Institute of Economics, most of them bearing my name. My main activity on the research front at this moment is to perfect my nonplex method for the solution of non-convex programming problems. This work has been wholeheartedly supported by the Norwegian Computing Center. It is hoped that a report of the results of this research may be published in the not too distant future.

I wish to express my gratitude to all those who have cooperated in the publication of the present book. In the first place, I am greatly indebted to my friend and colleague and former pupil, Professor Leif Johansen, now my successor as director of the University of Oslo Institute of Economics. Relying on notes taken by him as a student in 1953 during my course in the Oslo University, he has checked and improved the Norwegian text. This text was subsequently enlarged by some new developments which I added at the time of one of my sojourns in Paris, in the spring of 1957. This material formed the basis of the French edition published in 1960. The English edition is in all essentials identical with the French edition, with the exception that a number of misprints have now been corrected. Hopefully we may believe that not too many new ones have been introduced.

I also owe a debt of gratitude to my young friend Mr. Håvard Alstadheim, amanuensis in the University of Oslo Institute of Economics. He knows all the ins and outs of my published and as yet unpublished thoughts on an advanced form of macroeconomic planning, and he is thoroughly familiar with the type of reasoning contained in the present book, so essential as a basis for the theory of macroeconomic programming. Mr. Alstadheim is responsible for the checking and correcting of the MS of the English translation, and for correcting the page proofs.

My thanks are also due to Professor A. Nataf who furnished the examples given at end of each chapter.

Last but not least my thanks are due to Express Translation Service who presented a first draft of the English translation, and to Mr. Antonius Reidel and his associates in the D. Reidel Publishing Company of Dordrecht-Holland for the excellent job they have done in producing this edition.

Oslo, November 1965   RAGNAR FRISCH

TABLE OF CONTENTS

CHAPTER I

PRELIMINARY OBSERVATIONS

CHAPTER II

MAXIMUM AND MINIMUM IN THE DISCRETE CASE – INTRODUCTION TO THE PROBLEM OF LINEAR PROGRAMMING

CHAPTER III

PRELIMINARY REMARKS ON THE DETERMINATION OF THE EXTREMA OF A CONTINUOUS FUNCTION OF ONE VARIABLE

CHAPTER IV

EXACT CONCEPTS CONCERNING
TAYLOR'S FORMULA AND THE EXTREMA
OF A FUNCTION OF ONE VARIABLE

CHAPTER V

THE NECESSARY CONDITION OF THE
FIRST ORDER IN THE CASE OF TWO OR MORE
VARIABLES, WITHOUT CONSTRAINTS

CHAPTER VI

THE NECESSARY CONDITION OF THE
FIRST ORDER IN THE CASE OF TWO OR MORE
VARIABLES WITH CONSTRAINTS

CHAPTER VII

SIMULTANEOUS SEARCH FOR THE EXTREMA OF
SEVERAL FUNCTIONS – PARETO OPTIMALITY

CHAPTER VIII

LINEAR EQUATIONS

CHAPTER IX

LINEAR RELATIONS BETWEEN VECTORS, BETWEEN FUNCTIONS, AND BETWEEN EQUATIONS

CHAPTER X

SECOND-ORDER CONDITION AND SUFFICIENT CRITERION FOR LOCAL EXTREMUM IN THE CASE OF TWO VARIABLES WITHOUT CONSTRAINTS

CHAPTER XI

SECOND-ORDER CONDITIONS AND SUFFICIENT CRITERIA FOR THE LOCAL EXTREMUM IN THE CASE OF SEVERAL VARIABLES WITHOUT CONSTRAINTS

CHAPTER XII

SECOND-ORDER CONDITIONS AND SUFFICIENT CRITERIA FOR THE LOCAL EXTREMUM IN THE CASE OF SEVERAL VARIABLES WITH CONSTRAINTS

CHAPTER XIII

A BRIEF ACCOUNT OF THE THEORY OF MATRICES AND
OF THE CALCULATION OF DETERMINANTS

PRELIMINARY OBSERVATIONS

The role of mathematics

First, let us point out the importance of the mathematical theory of maxima and minima in economical and statistical analysis, and more generally the role of mathematics in the sphere of economics and statistics.

Usually the public learns of these methods from the newspapers, or else from people who are not trained in mathematics themselves and who have never applied mathematics to investigations in these fields. Thus one encounters the most absurd misunderstandings concerning the service mathematics can – or is supposed to – render to the subject.

These "explanations" are always fashionable. It seems that with a number of people unacquainted with mathematics it has become an obsession to turn the question over and over again. On the other hand, those who themselves actually use mathematics as a tool in their work hardly ever participate in the debate. Apparently they think it is not worth it, because they know – and the progress which is taking place in every country justifies them – that nothing can arrest the development of mathematical applications in economics and in statistics. The issues become gradually clearer as the number of users grows and their practical experience increases.

Maybe, however, these people appear too passive in the general discussion, and therefore it is not useless to say a few words on the subject.

I think all competent persons would agree on the following points:

The trend to develop the application of mathematics will follow its course without having to examine how devoid of value is every idea that cannot be formulated in mathematical terms. It will also always be necessary to consider the economical and statistical problems from the angle of philosophy, history and ideology, and in the light of concrete descriptions. The perspective should be widely open in both directions.

The problems considered call unquestionably for a verbal discussion which will furnish material, i.e. will bring forth factors one has to take into consideration.

But it is not enough to list the facts: we have to see them in their connections. To grasp the effect of the interaction of the different factors or to investigate the complex forms of causality one has to turn to mathematics so as to set in order and systematize the analysis. In these cases verbal discussion will never achieve a penetrating analysis. All attempts to do so will only lead to idle talk. There are no examples where an analysis including a considerable number of factors, or having a truly complex form of causality can be followed through without turning in one way or other to mathematical language.

That the interconnections have to be formulated in mathematical terms does not necessarily mean that they are based on exactly determined data. On the contrary, the same mathematical tools can be used to express the fact that the formulae are only approximations, and even to express the degree of accuracy.

If, starting from a given reality, one only takes into consideration a few simple and striking relations intending to make them understandable to the greatest number of people, a verbal – or essentially verbal – analysis proves to be very often a great success. The Keynesian models, developed in the thirties are good examples in this respect. They were constructed on the basis of a consumption function, an investment function, a liquidity-preference function, and some other simple concepts. But an apparatus of such elementary concepts reveals itself entirely insufficient for the complex and differentiated problems one is facing if one attempts to formulate an adequate economic policy applying to post-war society. This implies harmonisation of many antagonistic interests, consideration of many sectors of production, many social categories, etc. In the face of these problems, (if one really wants to see the facts in their inter-connections) one must turn to mathematical analysis in one form or another.

Although in the course of an analysis we have to use a mathematical formulation, we should strive to express the results in a form that is accessible to the public. Better still, we can suggest a demonstration by appealing to intuitive reasoning and everyday experience. Such popularisation is desirable, but nothing can be more dangerous than leaning

2

exclusively on this type of intuition. It has no value without rigorous reasoning on which it is based, and by which it is verified.

In this study we shall survey the problems of maximum and minimum, for functions of one or several variables, with or without constraints on the variables. This branch of mathematics has many applications in economics and statistics. It will be enough to think for instance of the problems arising when it is required to balance production and consumption in a free market or under other conditions, in connection with the distribution of the labour force when we have full employment, the construction of optimal estimators in statistics, etc. In fact it would be easier to quote the cases where we do not find maximum and minimum problems, than trying to enumerate the ones which pose this kind of problem.

Distinction between necessary and sufficient conditions

In what follows we shall attach great importance to two things which we consider essential: in the first place, to state clearly the *basic assumptions* required for the various manipulations; e.g. the condition of continuity for certain functions; in the second place, *to distinguish clearly between necessary and sufficient conditions*. Even otherwise excellent works fail precisely on these two points. It is rather easy to determine the necessary conditions for a maximum or a minimum. On the other hand, it is much less easy to define the sufficient conditions – at least when we are dealing with functions of several variables. As for determining conditions necessary and sufficient at the same time, this is so intricate that it makes hardly any sense to occupy oneself with it in a rather too general scheme.

Sometimes, we shall be led to formulate our analysis with the help of determinants and matrices. It has been debated many a time whether it is useful to introduce these concepts in the teaching of economics. In fact, experience shows that it is difficult to do without them.

We shall endeavour to *state* clearly the theorems which we shall rely upon even if we do not always furnish rigorous proofs. In fact, the proof of a theorem is occasionally very arduous, while its contents are simple and evident. There are numerous theorems of this kind, which possess a great analytical power. If only the reader assimilates a certain number of

3

these propositions, he will be ready to follow without too much effort, a relatively difficult analysis.

Maximum and minimum: extremal problems

First, some remarks on the terminology. The arguments used to find the *maximum* of a function are, essentially, similar to those used to determine its *minimum*.

Moreover, in many cases a maximum problem can be easily transformed into a minimum problem and conversely, by introducing a new function $g = -f$ or $g = 1/f$ to take the place of the initial function f.

Frequently one has to consider a set of points which are *either* maxima *or* minima. We denote these by the common term: *extrema*. Likewise, an *extremal problem* may denote either a maximum-problem or a minimum-problem.

Neighbourhood

We distinguish between *global* and *local* extrema. We may define the difference between global and local in the following way:

A point is an extremum in the global sense if it appears as an extremum in comparison with all the other points situated within the limits of a domain given in advance.

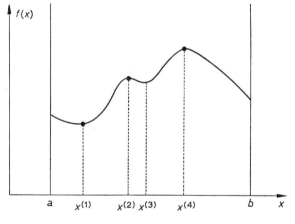

Fig. (1.1)

4

A point is an extremum in the local sense if one can *choose* a neighbourhood of this point in such a way that the point will appear as an extremum in comparison with other points situated in this neighbourhood. Thus in the case of a global definition the comparison is established with all points contained in a domain *given in advance*, whereas in the case of a local definition the comparison is restricted to a "locality" which we can *choose as small as we wish*.

The difference between the global definition and the local definition is illustrated by Figure (1.1). Here $f(x)$ is a function of x which we consider in the interval from a to b. (We shall examine later to what extent is it convenient to take account of the end points a and b). In this figure, $x^{(1)}$ and $x^{(3)}$ represent the local minima, $x^{(2)}$ and $x^{(4)}$ the local maxima. Thus, these four points form the set of local extrema. Let us take, for example, the point $x^{(2)}$: it is clearly possible to *choose* around this point a restricted neighbourhood such that in it $x^{(2)}$ will appear as a maximum. Nevertheless, among the four points, only $x^{(1)}$ represents a *global* minimum, and only $x^{(4)}$ a *global* maximum.

Strong and weak sense

Moreover, we shall distinguish between *strong* extrema and *weak* extrema. These distinctions apply both to local and global extrema. For a maximum, the difference between strong and weak may be formulated in this way:

The point $x^{(0)}$ is a strong maximum, if within the limits of the domain

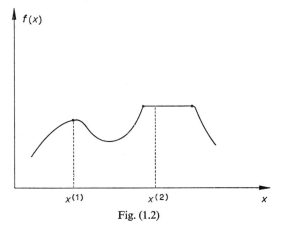

Fig. (1.2)

of definition (a domain given in advance if we are looking for a *global maximum*; a chosen neighbourhood if we are looking for a *local maximum*) at no point is $f(x)$ as large as at $x^{(0)}$. Thus everywhere in the domain under consideration, the function is *effectively smaller* than at $x^{(0)}$.

The point $x^{(0)}$ is a weak maximum if, within the limits of the domain of reference, at no point is $f(x)$ larger than at $x^{(0)}$. But one may find points at which the function has the same value as at $x^{(0)}$.

This distinction is illustrated by figure (1.2), where $x^{(1)}$ is a strong local maximum, and $x^{(2)}$ is a weak local maximum since the curve is horizontal on both sides of $x^{(2)}$.

Remarks on the necessary and sufficient conditions

Let c and C be two types of conditions, such that c is satisfied whenever C is, but not conversely. Then we may say that C is a *stronger* or *more exacting* condition than c.

Next, let us imagine that A is a property which we wish to subject to conditions. Let us suppose that we had at first ascertained that c is a *necessary* condition for A, and that we have proved that C is also a necessary condition for A. The proposition which we can thus state is more powerful than the previous one. We can now say: To have A, we must have not only c, but also C. Therefore we have an improvement, namely, we have *strenghtened* a necessary condition.

On the other hand, let us now look at sufficient conditions. Let us suppose that we had previously ascertained that C is a *sufficient* condition for a certain property B – for which we want to find conditions – and that afterwards we have established that c also is sufficient for B. The proposition which we can thus state is more general than the previous one. We can now say: B is realised not only when C is realised, but even when c alone is. Therefore we have an improvement, namely we have weakened a sufficient condition.

To have conditions which are necessary and sufficient *at the same time*, we can either gradually strengthen a necessary condition, i.e. work out *new requirements* until the conditions become also *sufficient*; or, which comes to the same thing, we can gradually weaken sufficient conditions, i.e. *eliminate all superfluous requirements* until the remaining conditions become *necessary*.

CHAPTER I

EXAMPLE

EXAMPLE (1.1)

We shall illustrate these considerations with a concrete example.

The condition A will be that a person, Peter, lives in the town of Baltimore.

The type of conditions C or c which we envisage will be conditions of Peter's geographic residence in regions smaller and smaller, containing the town of Baltimore, until these regions become identical with Baltimore.

A first necessary condition C_1, very insufficient, will be that Peter lives on the American continent.

A second condition C_2 will be that Peter lives in the United States.

A third, C_3, that Peter lives in the State of Maryland.

A fourth, C_4, is that, in this state, Peter lives in the largest town, which happens to be Baltimore.

The conditions C_1, C_2, C_3, C_4 are more and more restrictive: C_2 implies C_1; C_3 implies C_2; C_4 implies C_3 and is identical with A.

No doubt it may seem superfluous to find a set of rather complicated conditions for A, to arrive finally at C_4 which is identical with A. But it must be pointed out, that on the one hand the example has been given to show clearly in a pure form the general method of successive restrictions of the domain satisfying the necessary conditions C, and that on the other hand, one can present the condition A in a form less pure, but more natural, which shows the importance of the method of successive restrictions of necessary conditions.

For example, let us consider the following situation A. Peter wants to be as near as possible to his aged parents who live in a remote corner S of Maryland. Moreover, Peter specialises in building and management of department stores. Peter thus can settle only in a town large enough for a department store to succeed and which is also as near as possible to the locality S where his parents live. Therefore one has to choose in the neighbourhood C' of the State of Maryland the city nearest to S. It is clear that in C' it is Baltimore which satisfies all these conditions best.

In the rest of this book (e.g. in the study of linear programmes) we shall find other examples – identical in substance, but obviously less simple in appearance – of the restrictions of necessary conditions to more and more limited domains.

As an exercise, the reader might look for an example of sufficient conditions, in which one gets rid of the superfluous requirements until the remaining ones become necessary. One might for example develop the fact that to be born in Paris, it is sufficient to be born in one of the districts of Paris, a fact no doubt very trivial, but which is nevertheless constantly used in practice, because the legal proof of being a Parisian by birth is furnished by the possession of a birth certificate issued by one of the twenty districts of Paris.

MAXIMUM AND MINIMUM IN THE DISCRETE CASE. INTRODUCTION TO THE PROBLEM OF LINEAR PROGRAMMING

Discrete values

The maximum and minimum problems of functions which take only discrete values are often omitted from the usual treatises. Now, we are interested not only in the continuous case, and we shall pause for a moment at the discrete case, in order that we should obtain some indications of the situation.

Let f_x be a function of x defined for certain discrete values of x, e.g. $x = 1, 2, 3, ..., n$. To find a global extremum in this domain, one could, in principle, undertake to calculate first the values of f_x at all points, and then to compare all the values thus obtained. Or, one could look for a local extremum in a neighbourhood defined by the adjacent values of x. The most restricted neighbourhood of a given point x which we can choose is limited by the points nearest to the x on the near side and far side of x. In Figure (2.1), where f_x is defined for $x = 1, 2, 3, ..., 8$, we see for example, that $x = 4$ is a local maximum, and, further, that $x = 2$ and $x = 5$ are local minima.

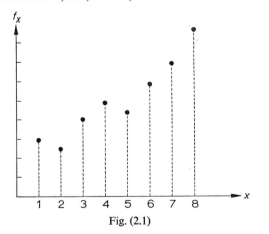

Fig. (2.1)

Yet, even in the discrete case, it is often possible to find the extrema by a method less tedious than the one which consists of calculating f_x, for the purpose of comparison, at each point x. If the numbers vary in a nearly regular manner, one may succeed in determining the difference $f_x - f_{x-1}$ or the ratio f_x/f_{x-1}, and by this means one may study the growth of the function. For example, we shall have a local maximum at a point where the difference $f_x - f_{x-1}$ changes from positive to negative; or where the ratio f_x/f_{x-1} formerly greater than 1, becomes less than 1 in a domain where f_x is positive. The situation is analogous for a local minimum.

EXAMPLE

EXAMPLE (2.1)

We shall study the maximum of the expression

$$f(x) = \binom{n}{x} p^x (1 - p)^{n-x}.$$

with respect to the integral variable x

$$x = 0, 1, ..., n$$

(p is strictly between 0 and 1).

We remark for the readers who are not familiar with it that $\binom{n}{x}$ is defined by

$$\binom{n}{x} = \frac{n!}{x! \, (n - x)!}$$

where $x! = 1 \times 2 \times 3 \times ... x$ is the product of the x first positive integers. $\binom{n}{0} = 1$ by definition.

Let us now calculate the ratio $f(x)/f(x - 1)$ which we shall denote by r_x, and which is defined whenever $f(x)$ and $f(x - 1)$ exist simultaneously, i.e. when x takes one of the n values $= 1, ..., (n - 1), n$ (but is not zero).

We have

$$r_x = \frac{f(x)}{f(x - 1)} = \frac{\dfrac{n!}{x! \, (n - x)!} p^x (1 - p)^{n-x}}{\dfrac{n!}{(x - 1)! \, [n - (x - 1)]!} p^{(x-1)} (1 - p)^{[n-(x-1)]}}$$

$$r_x = \frac{(x - 1)! \, [n - (x - 1)]!}{x! \, (n - x)!} \frac{p}{1 - p}$$

$$= \frac{[1 \cdot 2 \cdots (x - 1)] \, 1 \cdot 2 \cdots (n - x) \, [n - (x - 1)]}{(1 \cdot 2 \cdots x) \, 1 \cdot 2 \cdots (n - x)} \frac{p}{1 - p}$$

$$r_x = \frac{n - (x - 1)}{x} \frac{p}{1 - p} \tag{1}$$

$$r_x = \left[\frac{n+1}{x} - 1\right]\frac{p}{1-p} \tag{2}$$

Since the fraction $(n + 1)/x$ decreases as x its denominator increases, one sees from (2) that r_x is a steadily decreasing function of the integral variable x. The function $f(x)$ itself will increase if r_x is greater than 1, and decrease if r_x is less than 1. Given the fact that r_x decreases, $f(x)$ will pass through a maximum when r_x passes from a value greater than one to a value less than one.

To settle the problem, we shall ask ourselves: for what value x' of x is $r_x = 1$? We have:

$$\frac{n+1-x'}{x'}\frac{p}{1-p} = 1$$

$$(n + 1 - x')p = x'(1 - p)$$

$$(n + 1)p - x'p = x' - px'$$

thus

$$x' = (n + 1)p. \tag{3}$$

Since p is contained strictly between 0 and 1, i.e. it does not take the extreme values, the x' defined by (3) is contained between 0 and $(n + 1)$.

But we must remember that x varies from 1 to n, (bounds included) through integral values.

Thus we see that there are essentially three cases to be distinguished, according to the position of x' with respect to $1, 2, \ldots , n$

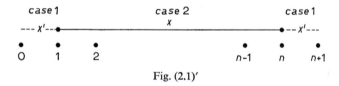

Fig. (2.1)′

1. If x' is contained between 0 and 1 or between n and $(n + 1)$, i.e. if $p < 1/(n + 1)$ or $p > (n + 1 - 1)/(n + 1)$, $p > 1 - (1/(n + 1))$ (briefly if p is very small or very large with respect to its extreme lower and upper bound). By inspecting the expression for r_x we find that:

$$r_x \text{ throughout is less than 1 when } \quad p < \frac{1}{n+1} \quad \text{ and } \quad x \geq 1$$

$$r_x \text{ throughout exceeds 1} \quad \text{ when } \quad p > 1 - \frac{1}{n+1} \quad \text{ and } \quad x \leq n$$

which implies that $f(x)$ decreases throughout in the first case, and increases throughout in the second case.

10

2. If x' is between 1 and n, without being an integer, that is, if

$$\frac{1}{n+1} < p < 1 - \frac{1}{n+1} \qquad p \neq \frac{k}{n+1} \qquad (k \text{ an integer})$$

we denote by l the greatest integer not exceeding x'.

$$x'$$

$$\overset{\cdot\ \cdot\ \cdot}{0\ 1\ 2} \quad \overset{\cdot}{l} \quad \overset{\cdot\cdot}{l+1} \quad \overset{\cdot}{n} \quad \overset{\cdot}{n+1}$$

For $x = 1, 2, \ldots l$ and $r_x > 1, f(x)$ increases; for $x = l + 1, \ldots, n - 1, n$ and $r_x < 1$, $f(x)$ decreases. Thus $f(x)$ is maximal for $x = l$.

3. Finally, if x' happens to be equal to one of the integers $1, 2, \ldots, n$, we write $x' = l + 1$

$$r_x \begin{cases} \text{will exceed 1 for } x = 1, 2, \ldots, l, \\ \text{is equal to 1 for } x = l + 1, \\ \text{is less than 1 for } x = l + 2, l + 3, \ldots, n. \end{cases}$$

Thus $f(x)$ will increase as x increases from 1 to l, $f(x)$ takes the same value (or one might say is stationary) for

$$x = l \quad \text{and} \quad l + 1,$$

$f(x)$ will decrease as x increases from $l + 1$ to n. Thus $f(x)$ will be maximal for $x = l$ and $x = l + 1$.

Graphical representation

The general case is illustrated by two figures: figure $(2.2)'$ for $n = 4, p = 1/10$ and figure $(2.3)'$ for $n = 6, p = 1/4$, corresponding respectively to the first and second case. We advise the reader to consider by himself an example of the third case, e.g. $n = 5$ and $p = 3/5$.

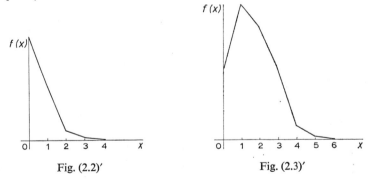

Fig. $(2.2)'$ Fig. $(2.3)'$

Formulation of the problem of linear programming

In certain cases, in discussing a problem which is in itself a continuous one, one is led to employing analytical techniques involving a discrete component. One such example is the problem of linear programming.

11

One can state this problem, briefly, in the following way: We have K variables $x_1, x_2, ..., x_K$ and we are looking for the maximum of

(2.2) $$f = p_1 x_1 + p_2 x_2 + \cdots + p_K x_K$$

where $p_1, p_2, ..., p_K$ are constants (not all zero) and $x_1, x_2, ..., x_K$ are variables, which are subject to two sets of constraints:

(1) A system of H equations

(2.3)
$$
\begin{aligned}
a_{11} x_1 + a_{12} x_2 + \cdots + a_{1K} x_K &= v_1 \\
a_{21} x_1 + a_{22} x_2 + \cdots + a_{2K} x_K &= v_2 \\
&\cdots\cdots\cdots\cdots\cdots\cdots\cdots \\
a_{H1} x_1 + a_{H2} x_2 + \cdots + a_{HK} x_K &= v_H
\end{aligned}
$$

where a_{hk} $(h=1, 2, ..., H; k=1, 2, ..., K)$ and v_h $(h=1, 2, ..., H)$ are given constants $(H \leqslant K)$;

(2) A system of K inequalities (bounds)

(2.4) $$x_k \geqslant 0 \qquad\qquad (k = 1, 2, ..., K).$$

We assume that the equations (2.3) are linearly independent, and consistent. A wide class of problems can be reduced to the form (2.2–4). Under the conditions which we have stated, the following fundamental theorem is valid.

Fundamental theorem concerning the solutions of the problem of linear programming

THEOREM (2.5). A point $x_1, x_2, ..., x_k$ is finite, if all its coordinates $x_1, x_2, ..., x_k$ are finite. This stated, every finite point which is a (global) maximum* for the linear form (2.2) subject to the constraints (2.3) and (2.4), either has the property that at least $(K-H)$ of its coordinates are zero, or it appears as a positive weighted average (positive weights with unit sum) of two or more maxima having the said property.

REMARK. $K-H$ is the number of the degrees of freedom for the

---

* In a linear programming problem we may either have one uniquely determined global maximum in the strong sense (the usual case) or we may have an infinite number of global maxima in the weak sense. We can never have a point which is only a local but not a global maximum.

12

problem, since there are H equations, assumed to be linearly independent and consistent. The inequalities do not reduce the number of degrees of freedom.

In virtue of (2.5), we could theoretically consider employing the following method: we choose in every possible way $K-H$ unknowns among the K variables x_1, x_2, ..., x_k – which can be done in $\binom{K}{K-H} = \binom{K}{H}$ different ways – and for each choice we put each of the selected $K-H$ unknowns equal to zero; we substitute these values into (2.3) and investigate whether the system of equations obtained in this way has a solution for the remaining H variables. If this is the case, we determine these values of x. (When the solutions contain a certain number of arbitrary parameters, the details are rather complicated, and we shall not discuss them here.)

From the set of points thus determined, we exclude those which do not satisfy (2.4). At each of the remaining points we will evaluate the linear form (2.2), and we will choose the one, or the ones, at which f attains its maximum value. In this way one obtains a maximum, or a set of maxima – namely all the maxima which have the property that at least $K-H$ of their coordinates are exactly zero.

Clearly, the technique employed in the last part of the calculation is of a discrete character, since we evaluate f for a discrete set of points, and establish a direct comparison between the values of f obtained in this way.

In the case when, following this method, we obtain several points giving a maximum value for f, each linear combination of these points formed with positive coefficients of unit sum will also be a maximum.

To prove the accuracy of the preceding assertion, we assume that the coordinates

$$(2.6) \qquad x_1^{(j)}, x_2^{(j)}, ..., x_K^{(j)} \qquad (j = 1, 2, ... J)$$

represent J points giving the maximum value of f, and satisfying the conditions (2.3) and (2.4). We have now

$$(2.7) \qquad \sum_{k=1}^{K} a_{hk} x_k^{(j)} = v_h \qquad (h = 1, 2, ..., H; j = 1, 2, ..., J)$$

and

$$(2.8) \qquad x_k^{(j)} \geqslant 0 \qquad (k = 1, 2, ..., K; j = 1, 2, ..., J)$$

13

We define a new point by

$$(2.9) \quad x_k = \alpha_1 x_k^{(1)} + \alpha_2 x_k^{(2)} + \cdots + \alpha_J x_k^{(J)} = \sum_{j=1}^{J} \alpha_j x_k^{(j)} \quad (k = 1, 2, ..., K)$$

where $\alpha_1, \alpha_2, ..., \alpha_J$ are arbitrary numbers satisfying

$$(2.10) \qquad \alpha_j \geqslant 0 \quad (j = 1, 2, ..., J) \quad \text{and} \quad \sum_{j=1}^{J} \alpha_j = 1 .$$

Then we observe that the new point defined in this way satisfies the condition (2.4) of non-negativity. In order to see whether this new point also satisfies (2.3), we substitute (2.9) into the left-hand side of (2.3). This gives

$$\sum_{k=1}^{K} a_{hk} x_k = \sum_{k=1}^{K} a_{hk} \sum_{j=1}^{J} \alpha_j x_k^{(j)} = \sum_{j=1}^{J} \alpha_j \sum_{k=1}^{K} a_{hk} x_k^{(j)},$$

which is equal to $\sum_{j=1}^{J} \alpha_j v_h = v_h$ when (2.7) and (2.10) are valid. The new point given by (2.9) thus satisfies both (2.3) and (2.4).

We investigate the value of f at the new point. We have

$$f = \sum_{k=1}^{K} p_k x_k = \sum_{k=1}^{K} p_k \sum_{j=1}^{J} \alpha_j x_k^{(j)} = \sum_{j=1}^{J} \alpha_j \left(\sum_{k=1}^{K} p_k x_k^{(j)} \right) = \sum_{j=1}^{J} \alpha_j f_{max} = f_{max},$$

where f_{max} is the maximum value of f (equal to the value of f at each of the points given by (2.6)).

The preceding reasoning shows that if the points (2.6) are maxima, the points given by (2.9), where the $\alpha_1, \alpha_2, ... \alpha_J$ satisfy (2.10), are also maxima. On the other hand, the theorem (2.5) asserts that if (2.6) is a set of maxima, complete in a certain sense (i.e. comprising all the maxima where at least $(K-H)$ of the coordinates are strictly zero), all the points which give the maximum of f can be represented in the form (2.9).

In most cases, the technique which we have just described is only of theoretical interest, since its application would entail an inordinate amount of work. More rational methods have been developed for the solution of the maximum problems of linear programming, but we shall not consider them here.

PRELIMINARY REMARKS
ON THE DETERMINATION OF THE EXTREMA OF A
CONTINUOUS FUNCTION OF ONE VARIABLE

When one discusses the maximum and minimum of a function of one variable, it would be unwise to consider this problem as *solved* by the simple act of putting the derivative equal to zero. This procedure is often, but not always correct. Thus, one should proceed with the greatest caution, and investigate more closely the different kind of situations which can arise. We shall illustrate this graphically, and in doing this will provisionally accept a purely intuitive concept of the derivative, considered as the slope of the tangent.

Horizontal tangent

Let us reason in this way: If the slope of the tangent is *positive*, we can increase the value of the function, by going to the right; if the slope of the tangent is *negative*, we can increase the value of the function by going to the left. Hence, where the curve has a local maximum, the tangent must be horizontal.

This reasoning is only correct if two essential conditions are fulfilled: first, that the slope of the tangent varies continuously in the domain under consideration; secondly, that we do *not* include the end-points of the interval where the function is defined. Then, we can consider the points situated on both sides of the point studied, and we can make use of the following theorem (theorem of separation):

THEOREM (3.1). If a function of x (in this case, the derivative) is positive at a certain point x, and negative at another point x', and is continuous, then this function is zero at least at one intermediate point.

Figure (3.2) illustrates one case when a function $f(x)$ has a maximum without its derivative being zero. The upper part of the diagram shows $f(x)$, the lower part $f'(x) = df(x)/dx$. $f(x)$ has a maximum at $x^{(0)}$ (at the angular point), but the derivative at this point is not zero. It has a discontinuity at $x^{(0)}$, passing from a positive value to a negative value.

On the other hand, if the derivative is continuous and if we exclude the end-points of the domain of definition of $f(x)$ from consideration, then for $f(x)$ to have a maximum (or a minimum) it is *necessary* that the derivative should vanish at the point of maximum (or minimum). This is a consequence of the principle of separation to which we have referred above.

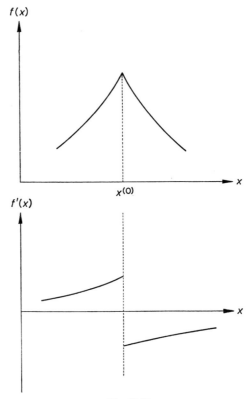

Fig. (3.2)

Stationary points

Thus, in the case when the derivative is continuous, and the end-points are excluded, we know that all the extrema will be found among the points where the derivative is zero. Consequently, if we are looking for the extrema, we can begin by considering the points where the derivative is zero, knowing that all the local extrema will be found necessarily *among* them. But we must beware of believing that all the points where the derivative is zero are necessarily points of extrema.

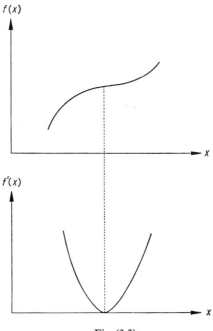

Fig. (3.3)

Figure (3.3) gives an example of a curve with a continuously varying tangent, and such that there is a point where the slope of the tangent is zero, but which is nevertheless not an extremum. The curve has here a point of inflexion with a horizontal tangent.

A point where the derivative is zero is sometimes called a *stationary point*.

To sum up our conclusions, we can say that every extremum is a stationary point, but not every stationary point is an extremum.

In certain cases, the answer to the question whether a given stationary point is or is not an extremum, depends on the meaning (*strong* or *weak* sense) which we give to the word "extremum". Let us consider for

17

example figure (3.4). Here, $f(x)$ is constant in the domain $x^{(0)} \leqslant x \leqslant x^{(1)}$. The derivative is continuous in the whole domain, provided that the tangent of the left-hand branch of the curve is horizontal at $x^{(0)}$, and that the tangent of the right-hand branch of the curve is horizontal at $x^{(1)}$. The

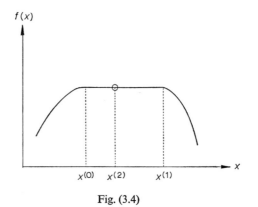

Fig. (3.4)

slope of the tangent of this curve is thus positive on the left-hand side of $x^{(0)}$, zero between $x^{(0)}$ and $x^{(1)}$ (the end-points included) and negative on the right-hand side of $x^{(1)}$. Whether $f(x)$ is considered to have a maximum at a point $x^{(2)}$, situated between $x^{(0)}$ and $x^{(1)}$, depends on the meaning which we give to the term "maximum": that is, whether we understand it in the strong sense or in the weak sense (Compare with Preliminary remarks). According to the "strong" definition, the curve does not have a local maximum at $x^{(2)}$. But if we understand "maximum" in the weak sense, we can say that $f(x)$ has a local maximum at every point $x^{(2)}$ situated between $x^{(0)}$ and $x^{(1)}$, the end-points included.

End-points. Open interval and closed interval

Let us pause for a moment to consider the end-points, i.e. the boundary points which limit the domain of definition of $f(x)$. Let us imagine that we consider a function $f(x)$ inside the domain (a, b), as is shown in figure (3.5). The problem is to know if we can say that $f(x)$ has an extremum here. The answer depends on this: is the interval (a, b) *open* or *closed*? We define an interval as open if it does not contain its end-points;

18

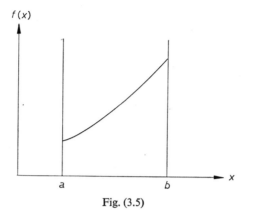

Fig. (3.5)

in other words an open interval is the set of all points x, for which

(3.6) $a < x < b$ (definition of the open interval).

We define an interval as closed if it contains its end-points; in other words, a closed interval is the set of all points x, for which

(3.7) $a \leqslant x \leqslant b$ (definition of the closed interval).

Of course the interval could be closed at one end and open at the other, but it would be pointless to consider this case here. If we choose (3.6), i.e. the open interval, we can say that $f(x)$ has in it *neither a maximum nor a minimum*, no more a local, than a global one. Indeed, if we choose any point, however near it is to b, we can always find another one which is even nearer to b, and thus gives a greater value for $f(x)$. The function has thus no maximum in the open interval (a, b). In the same way, we see that it has no minimum either.

Bounds. Exact bounds

On the other hand, we can say that in the present example, the function has in the interval an upper bound and a lower bound. If the function is continuous and monotonic in the interval, the smaller of the numbers $f(a)$ and $f(b)$ represents a lower bound, and the greater one an upper bound. In the present example the bounds are also *exact*, in the sense that it is possible to give in the interval values of x at which $f(x)$ approaches as closely as it is desired the values of these bounds.

19

If we choose (3.7), i.e. the closed interval, the function in figure (3.5) will have a minimum at a and a maximum at b, although $f'(x)$ is not zero at the end-points of the interval.

In what follows we shall in general exclude the case when the interval is considered as closed. That is the clearest way to carry out the analysis of extremal problems, and to train the reader how to handle the mathematical tools. Should the occasion arise that one wishes to take the end-points into consideration, one could, for example, simply calculate the values of the function at the end-points, and compare them directly with the values it takes elsewhere in the interval. As for concrete problems, it is in general very important to take the end-points – which may have a specific significance – into account, and it is advisable to carry out the above mentioned comparison of values.

The above examples show that the method of putting the derivatives equal to zero must not be applied mechanically, without circumspection.

EXACT CONCEPTS CONCERNING TAYLOR'S FORMULA AND THE EXTREMA OF A FUNCTION OF ONE VARIABLE

We shall now give up the intuitive reasoning (based on graphical representations) used in the preceding chapters, and will develop an exact argument instead.

This argument is based upon a certain property of a chord of a curve, and on a special application of the mean value theorem.

Let $f(x)$ be a continuous function with continuous (and hence bounded) derivatives of all orders considered. Let x^0 and x be two values of the variable x. (We can have $x > x^0$, or $x < x^0$). In virtue of the geometric property of the chord it is always possible to choose between x and x^0 at least one point ξ such that

(4.1)
$$f'(\xi) = \frac{f(x) - f(x^0)}{x - x^0}.$$

This formula asserts that the slope of the tangent at the point is equal to the slope of the chord joining x^0 and x. This is illustrated by figure (4.2) where the tangent at the point M is parallel to the line PQ.

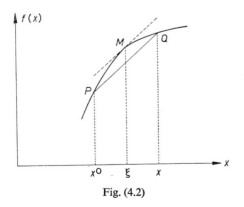

Fig. (4.2)

Taylor's formula in the case of one variable

Multiplying (4.1) by $(x - x_0)$ and rearranging the terms, we obtain

(4.3) $$f(x) = f(x^0) + f'(\xi)(x - x^0).$$

That is the exact form of the mean value theorem. If we interpret ξ as a *suitably chosen* value between x^0 and x, (4.3) becomes an exact *identity* for all functions with a continuous (and bounded) first derivative.

By a similar argument for the derivative we obtain the formula

(4.4) $$f(x) = f(x^0) + f'(x^0)(x - x^0) + \frac{1}{2} f''(\xi)(x - x^0)^2.$$

In this case the assumption is that $f''(x)$, the second derivative, is continuous (and bounded) in the interval under consideration. Moreover, in (4.4) ξ is situated between x and x^0, but clearly this ξ is different from the one in (4.3). If ξ is suitably chosen, (4.4) is again an exact identity.

Carrying on in the same way, we arrive at the general Taylor expansion:

(4.5) $$f(x) = f(x^0) + f'(x^0)(x - x^0) + \frac{1}{2!} f''(x^0)(x - x^0)^2 + \cdots$$

$$+ \frac{1}{(v-1)!} f^{(v-1)}(x^0)(x - x^0)^{v-1} + \frac{1}{v!} f^{(v)}(\xi)(x - x^0)^v.$$

The assumption in (4.5) is that the v-th derivative is continuous (and bounded). As in the previous case, ξ is situated between x and x^0, and if it is suitably chosen, the formula is an exact identity.

Having established these formulae, we are now in the position to carry out the precise arguments concerning the extremum of a function of one variable, assuming that the function has continuous derivatives up to a certain order (as many as we shall have to consider in each case).

The necessary condition of the first order for the case of one variable

First of all, we shall state a necessary condition for $x = x^0$ to give a local extremum. We rewrite (4.4) as:

(4.6) $$f(x) - f(x^0) = \left[f'(x^0) + \frac{1}{2} f''(\xi)(x - x^0) \right](x - x^0).$$

22

This formula is exact whatever the value given to x. In particular, we can choose x, such that the difference $(x - x^0)$ should be – in absolute value – as small as we wish. If $f''(\xi)$ is bounded (finite), we can now arrange (considering only such values of x which make $x - x^0$ smaller than a given number, i.e. restricting ourselves to a suitably defined neighbourhood around x^0) that in (4.6) $\frac{1}{2}f''(\xi)(x - x^0)$ should be smaller in absolute value than an arbitrary finite number.

Let us assume now that $f'(x^0) \neq 0$. According to what has been said above, we can always confine ourselves to consider around x^0 a neighbourhood sufficiently small to make the whole parenthesis in (4.6) have everywhere the same sign as $f'(x^0)$. It also follows that we can find in this neighbourhood points x such that we have $f(x) - f(x^0) > 0$, and other such that we have $f(x) - f(x^0) < 0$. Indeed we can choose an $x > x^0$, and also an $x < x^0$ within the limits of this neighbourhood. If $f'(x^0) \neq 0$, and the second derivative $f''(x)$ is continuous (and bounded) around x, $x = x^0$ cannot be an extremum for $f(x)$. We can state this fact in the form of the following theorem:

THEOREM (4.7). A necessary condition for a function $f(x)$ – having a continuous (and bounded) second derivative around the point x^0 – to have at this point a local extremum, is that the first derivative should be zero, i.e. that $f'(x^0) = 0$.

A sufficient condition in the case of one variable

Next, we shall state a *sufficient* condition for the extrema. We apply (4.5) for $v = 3$. Making use of the necessary condition $f'(x^0) = 0$, we obtain

$$(4.8) \quad f(x) - f(x^0) = \frac{1}{2}\left[f''(x^0) + \frac{1}{3}f'''(\xi)(x - x^0)\right](x - x^0)^2.$$

If we assume that $f''(x^0) \neq 0$, and $f'''(x)$ is continuous (and hence bounded) in the interval, we see, in the same way as in (4.6), that we can always choose a sufficiently small neighbourhood for which in Formula (4.8) the square bracket has everywhere the same sign as $f''(x^0)$. We shall make use of this observation in discussing the extremum.

First we assume that $f''(x^0)$ is strictly negative. In virtue of what has been said above, and the fact that $(x - x^0)^2 > 0$, whenever $|x - x^0| > 0$, it follows that it is possible to choose a neighbourhood around x^0 in such a way, that $f(x)-f(x^0)<0$ at every point of this neighbourhood, except for the point $x=x^0$, where obviously $f(x)=f(x^0)$. Hence we can state the following theorem:

THEOREM (4.9). A sufficient condition for a function $f(x)$ – having a continuous (and bounded) third derivative around the point x^0 – to have a local maximum at this point is that $f(x^0)=0$ and that $f''(x^0)<0$.

In a completely similar way we have:

THEOREM (4.10). A sufficient condition for a function $f(x)$ – having a continuous (and bounded) third derivative around the point x^0 – to have a local minimum at this point is that $f'(x^0)=0$, and that $f''(x^0)>0$.

If we combine (4.9) and (4.10), we see that we can formulate a sufficient condition for extrema, simply by replacing the condition for the second derivative by $f''(x^0)\neq0$.

A strengthened necessary condition

The conditions (4.9–10) are *sufficient* but not necessary. By weakening the condition concerning $f''(x^0)$, we can obtain conditions which are necessary and stronger than the condition (4.7) – but not sufficient. For this, we replace the condition $f''(x^0)<0$ by $f''(x^0)\leqslant0$ and $f''(x^0)>0$ by the condition $f''(x^0)\geqslant0$. The replacement in these conditions of the symbols $<$ or $>$ by $\leqslant$ or $\geqslant$ clearly results in the *weakening* of the conditions. Hence the following theorems:

THEOREM (4.11). A necessary condition for a function $f(x)$ – having a continuous (and bounded) third derivative around the point x^0 – to have a local maximum at this point is that $f'(x^0)=0$, and $f''(x^0)\leqslant0$.

THEOREM (4.12). A necessary condition for a function $f(x)$ – having a continuous (and bounded) third derivative around the point x^0 – to have a local minimum at this point is that $f'(x^0) = 0$, and that $f''(x^0) \geqslant 0$.

The difference between the sufficiency expressed by (4.9–10) and the necessity, expressed by (4.11–12), is thus due solely to introducing the sign of equality into the conditions on the second derivative.

The justification of (4.11) is the following: Theorem (4.7) asserts that for x^0 to be a maximum it is necessary that $f'(x^0)=0$, theorem (4.10) asserts that if $f'(x^0)=0$ and $f''(x^0)>0$, x^0 is a minimum. For x^0 to be a maximum it is thus clearly *necessary* that the condition $f''(x^0)>0$

24

should not be fulfilled, and hence that $f''(x^0) \leqslant 0$, as stated in (4.11). An analogous reasoning gives the justification of (4.12).

A necessary and sufficient condition

Above we have proved theorems stating *sufficient* conditions for the maximum and minimum respectively (4.9–10), then theorems giving *necessary* conditions for the maximum and minimum of a function respectively (4.11–12). But we have not yet established a theorem stating conditions *necessary and sufficient* at the same time – conditions which can be found if we pursue our reasoning beginning with (4.5), in the same way as above. In this way we obtain the following theorems (it is always understood that all the derivatives which we need exist and are continuous):

THEOREM (4.13). A necessary and sufficient condition for a function $f(x)$ – having continuous (and bounded) derivatives of all order around a point x^0 – to have a local maximum at this point is that the first nonzero derivative should be of even order (at least of the second order), and negative.

THEOREM (4.14). A necessary and sufficient condition for a function $f(x)$ – having continuous (and bounded) derivatives of all order around a point x^0 – to have a local minimum at this point is that the first nonzero derivative should be of even order (at least of the second order), and positive.

These last theorems also clear up the case when $f'(x^0)=0$ and $f''(x^0)=0$, not explained by (4.9–12).

REMARK. Concerning 4.1, we expressed ourselves in this way: "Let $f(x)$ be a continuous function with continuous (*and also bounded*) derivatives...". The same expression is also used in other connections. Its meaning is always this: "Let $f(x)$ be a continuous function having continuous derivatives in the interior of the closed (finite) domain which we are considering – derivatives which are therefore also bounded in the interior of our domain..." When we consider a closed (finite) domain, continuity of a function implies its boundedness.

EXAMPLE

EXAMPLE (4.1)

Example on the maximum or minimum of a function of one variable. Discuss the maxima or minima when x varies from $-\infty$ to $+\infty$: (a) of the function $f_1(x) = e^{(x-2)^3}$, (b) of the function $f_2(x) = - e^{(x-2)^4}$.

We shall investigate these two problems first directly, in two different ways moreover, and then by applying theorems (4.13) and (4.14).

(a)
$$f_1(x) = e^{(x-2)^3}$$
$$f_1'(x) = 3(x-2)^2 e^{(x-2)^3}.$$

It is observed that $f_1'(x)$ vanishes for $x = 2$, but $f_1'(x)$ is positive for all values of x distinct from 2. Thus the function $f_1'(x)$ increases steadily from $-\infty$ to $+\infty$ and does not permit a local extremum.

If one discusses the problem by applying Theorem (4.13) and (4.14), one finds that the successive derivatives are of the form:

$$f_1''(x) = 3 \cdot 2 \cdot (x-2) e^{(x-2)^3} + 3 \cdot 3 \cdot (x-2)^4 e^{(x-2)^3}$$
$$f_1'''(x) = 3 \cdot 2 \, e^{(x-2)^3} + 3 \cdot 3 \cdot 2 (x-2)^3 e^{(x-2)^3} + 4 \cdot 3 \cdot 3 \cdot (x-2)^3 e^{(x-2)^3}$$
$$+ 3 \cdot 3 \cdot 3 (x-2)^6 e^{(x-2)^3}.$$

Thus, the first non-zero derivative at $x = 2$ is the third; its value is $f_2'''(2) = 6$. Consequently neither Theorem (4.13) nor Theorem (4.14) applies. $f_1(x)$ is simply stationary at $x = 2$.

(b)
$$f_2(x) = - e^{(x-2)^4}$$

$(x-2)^4$ is always positive, except for $x = 2$, where it is zero. Thus $- e^{(x-2)^4}$ is smallest in absolute value for $x = 2$, when $|f_2(2)| = +1$, and since $f_2(x)$ is always negative, $x = 2$ is an absolute maximum for $f_2(x)$, with $f_2(2) = -1$.

On applying Theorems (4.13) and (4.14), one finds that the first non-zero derivative at $x = 2$ (we leave the calculation of the derivatives to the reader) is the fourth derivative, and that $f_2^{\mathrm{IV}}(2)$ is negative. Thus, theorem (4.13) applies and the function $f_2(x)$ has a local maximum at $x = 2$.

One notes through these examples that what matters above all in these extremal problems in one variable is to discover the sign of $f'(x)$ around the extremum; and that furthermore it is often possible to investigate directly the variation of the functions considered; while the theorems (4.13) and (4.14), can always of course be applied.

CHAPTER V

THE NECESSARY CONDITION OF
THE FIRST ORDER IN THE CASE OF TWO OR MORE
VARIABLES, WITHOUT CONSTRAINTS

Graphical illustration. Intuitive concepts concerning the necessary conditions in the case of two variables

As a first step, we consider the diagram below (figure 5.1), which represents the level-curves of a function $f(x_1, x_2)$. By a level-curve is meant a curve along which the value of $f(x_1, x_2)$ remains constant. These curves have the same meaning as the contours of a map.

Since the "terrain" is continuous, it is evident that if there is an extremum, the level curves around this point will be closed curves, one

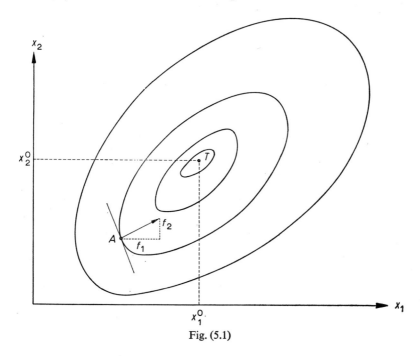

Fig. (5.1)

inscribed inside the other. In this picture every maximum of $f(x_1, x_2)$ is represented as a summit of the "terrain" and every minimum of $f(x_1, x_2)$ as a depression.

Let us consider an arbitrary point – e.g. A in Figure (5.1). We then draw the tangent to the level curve passing through this point, and construct a perpendicular to this tangent. This perpendicular – oriented positively in the direction in which the function $f(x_1, x_2)$ increases – can be conceived as a gradient whose components are the partial derivatives f_1 and f_2, defined by

$$(5.2) \quad f_1 = f_1(x_1, x_2) = \frac{\partial f(x_1, x_2)}{\partial x_1} \quad f_2 = f_2(x_1, x_2) = \frac{\partial f(x_1, x_2)}{\partial x_2}.$$

In particular, these components indicate that for small variations (dx_1, dx_2) of the given point, $df = f_1 dx_1 + f_2 dx_2$ will give, "as a first approximation", the variation of f. When we follow the direction of the gradient, we can say that we "climb the terrain along the steepest possible slope". In figure (5.1) the components of the gradient, f_1 and f_2 are drawn in such a way, as to indicate the direction of "ascent" (in the case when the level-curves represent a summit of the "terrain" and not a depression).

This intuitive manner of talking about "the slope of the terrain", which also implies notions like "the distance between two points", etc., supposes that the variables x_1 and x_2 have a concrete metric meaning, which forbids us to subject them to transformations like, for example, linear transformations. In fact, even a simple modification of the absolute values of x_1 and x_2 will falsify the measurements which give the expressions for the "slope of the land", the "distance between points", etc... But even when in a given case, we have not defined the variables in an absolute manner, and the statement of the problem does not assign numerical values to them, we still have the right to use the expressions like "slope of the terrain", "distance between two points", etc.... in a purely conventional sense, if this can help us to obtain a picture of what is happening in the graphical representation.

It is intuitively clear, when we consider Figure (5.1), that at the point T (i.e. at the point (x_1^0, x_2^0)) the components f_1 and f_2 of the gradient must necessarily *vanish*, i.e. become zero. In fact, if they do not vanish, it would be necessarily possible to go *beyond* the point T, to a new point where the function $f(x_1, x_2)$ would be greater, given that the increment of f, in the first approximation, is $f_1 dx_1 + f_2 dx_2$.

Taylor's formula in the case of two variables

We shall now verify rigorously that these intuitive conclusions are confirmed as exact ones for a very general class of problems. For this, we shall rely upon Taylor's formula for the case of two variables. Let (x_1, x_2) and (x_1^0, x_2^0) be two arbitrary points; the value of the function at the first of these points can be expressed with the help of the values of the function and its derivatives at the second point, in the following way:

$$f(x_1, x_2) = f^0 + [f_1^0 \xi_1 + f_2^0 \xi_2]$$
$$f(x_1, x_2) = f^0 + [f_1^0 \xi_1 + f_2^0 \xi_2] + \tfrac{1}{2}[f_{11}^0 \xi_1^2 + 2f_{12}^0 \xi_1 \xi_2 + f_{22}^0 \xi_2^2]$$
$$(5.3) \quad f(x_1, x_2) = f^0 + [f_1^0 \xi_1 + f_2^0 \xi_2] + \tfrac{1}{2}[f_{11}^0 \xi_1^2 + 2f_{12}^0 \xi_1 \xi_2 + f_{22}^0 \xi_2^2]$$
$$+ \tfrac{1}{3!}[f_{111}^\theta \xi_1^3 + 3f_{112}^\theta \xi_1^2 \xi_2 + 3f_{122}^\theta \xi_1 \xi_2^2 + f_{222}^\theta \xi_2^3],$$

where

$$\xi_1 = x_1 - x_1^0 \qquad \xi_2 = x_2 - x_2^0.$$

On the right-hand side of the identities (5.3), f denotes the value of the function, f_1 and f_2 the first derivatives as defined in (5.2), f_{ij} the second derivatives, and f_{ijk} the third derivatives, which are defined by the formula (5.4) below:

$$(5.4) \qquad f_{ij} = \frac{\partial^2 f}{\partial x_i \partial x_j} \qquad f_{ijk} = \frac{\partial^3 f}{\partial x_i \partial x_j \partial x_k}$$

The index ^{0} on the right-hand side of the formulae (5.3) indicates that the values of the arguments are (x_1^0, x_2^0). The index θ signifies that we substitute for the values of the arguments the values below:

$$(5.5) \qquad x_1^0 + \theta(x_1 - x_1^0) \quad \text{and} \quad x_2^0 + \theta(x_2 - x_2^0)$$

where θ is a suitably chosen number between 0 and 1, that is

$$(5.6) \qquad 0 \leqslant \theta \leqslant 1.$$

The formulae (5.5)–(5.6) say that the point substituted into the derivatives in the brackets on the right-hand side of the formulae (5.3), will be everywhere a suitably chosen point, situated on the segment joining (x_1^0, x_2^0) and (x_1, x_2). In other words, more precisely: on this segment one

29

can find (at least) one point such that if one substituted it for the argument of the derivatives in the last bracket on the right-hand side of the formulae (5.3), these formulae become exact *identities*. We cannot know in advance *which* point this is, and, in the majority of cases, we can say nothing more precise on this subject. Nevertheless, formulae (5.3) will turn out to be very important, because they allow us in a large number of cases, to give upper and lower bounds for the derivatives. From a formal point of view we can say that each formula of (5.3) defines θ as a (possibly many-valued) function of (x_1, x_2) and (x_1^0, x_2^0). The form of this function will depend on the form of the function f, but in all cases θ will *satisfy* (5.6). And that is the important fact.

The formulae (5.3) give successive approximations. The first line gives an approximation of zero order, the second line an approximation of the first order, etc. The term given in the last parenthesis – the one involving θ – can in every case be considered as a symbolic binomial expansion. For example, the last parenthesis in the last line of (5.3) can be written down by expanding $(\xi_1 + \xi_2)^3$ according to the binomial formula. Carrying out this expansion, one adds to each term the coefficient f_{ijk}^θ, where the lower index ijk contains the number 1 as many times as is indicated by the exponent of ξ_1 in the given term. For the remaining ones of the three lower indices ijk, one takes 2.

In the general case, the remainder term can also be written in the form:

$$(5.7) \qquad \frac{1}{\nu!} \sum_{i=1}^{2} \sum_{j=1}^{2} \cdots \sum_{k=1}^{2} f_{ij\cdots k}^\theta \xi_i \xi_j \cdots \xi_k.$$

The number of the summation indices $i, j, \ldots, k$ is ν; thus in the last line of (5.3), $\nu = 3$. In certain cases, Formula (5.7) will be more expedient than the binomial formula.

The correctness of the formulae (5.3) can easily be proved if we write the variables x_1 and x_2 in the form

$$(5.8) \qquad x_1^0 + s(x_1 - x_1^0) \qquad x_2^0 + s(x_2 - x_2^0).$$

This indicates that we should consider the function

$$f\left[x_1^0 + s(x_1 - x_1^0), \quad x_2^0 + s(x_2 - x_2^0)\right],$$

where x_1, x_2, and x_1^0, x_2^0 are the values occurring in (5.3). We now consider them as given. On the other hand, s is a new variable. We are very much interested in examining the variation of s between 0 and 1, because in this way we describe in the diagram the segment joining (x_1^0, x_2^0) and (x_1, x_2). If, using Taylor's formula (developed in Chapter IV) for the case of a single variable, we expand this function in a Taylor series with respect to s, we shall have

(5.9)
$$\frac{df}{ds} = f_1\xi_1 + f_2\xi_2$$
$$\frac{d^2f}{ds^2} = f_{11}\xi_1^2 + 2f_{12}\xi_1\xi_2 + f_{22}\xi_2^2$$
$$\frac{d^3f}{ds^3} = f_{111}\xi_1^3 + 3f_{112}\xi_1^2\xi_2 + 3f_{122}\xi_1\xi_2^2 + f_{222}\xi_2^3.$$

All the arguments on the right-hand side of the formulae (5.9) are those of (5.8).

If we now substitute these expressions into Taylor's formula for a function of a single variable, we obtain successively the expressions (5.3). For example, the last formula of (5.3) is derived from

(5.10)
$$f(x_1, x_2) - f(x_1^0, x_2^0) = \left(\frac{df}{ds}\right)_{s=0} \cdot 1 + \frac{1}{2!}\left(\frac{d^2f}{ds^2}\right)_{s=0} \cdot 1^2 + \frac{1}{3!}\left(\frac{d^3f}{ds^3}\right)_{s=\theta} \cdot 1^3 ,$$

in which θ is situated in the interval (5.6) and which gives the last formula of (5.3). The remaining formulae of (5.3) are proved in an analogous way. If one wishes, one can even obtain expressions of a higher order.

Exact concepts concerning the necessary conditions of the first order in the case of two variables

We now apply (5.3) to the study of the situation in the neighbourhood of a *maximum* (x_1^0, x_2^0) of the function $f(x_1, x_2)$. We *assume* now that the point (x_1^0, x_2^0) is a local maximum and we look for the necessary conditions which have to be satisfied in this case by the partial derivatives f_1 and f_2 at this point. Conforming to the definition of a local maximum, we can say in this analysis, that we limit ourselves to a neighbourhood of (x_1^0, x_2^0), which is as small as we wish.

We can define the extent of this neighbourhood in different ways. For

31

example, we can set up around the point (x_1^0, x_2^0) a small rectangle or a small circle. We shall use here a circle, and determine the size of the neighbourhood by specifying its radius – a radius which can be as small as we wish, as long as it is not exactly zero. Instead of saying that the point (x_1, x_2) is situated in the proximity of the point (x_1^0, x_2^0) – more precisely, inside the small circle encircling this point – we can in fact say that the point (ξ_1, ξ_2) (defined by (5.3)) is situated inside a small circle encircling the origin of the (ξ_1, ξ_2) plane. To do this, we proceed in the following way:

All the points situated inside a circle of radius R encircling the origin of the (ξ_1, ξ_2) plane can be represented by

$$(5.11) \qquad \xi_1 = rp_1 \qquad \xi_2 = rp_2,$$

where p_1 and p_2 are two numbers satisfying

$$(5.12) \qquad p_1^2 + p_2^2 = 1$$

and where r is a quantity less than the radius R of the circle defining the neighbourhood. For this problem it is also convenient to exclude the origin itself from the considered variation of (ξ_1, ξ_2). This is achieved by requiring that $r > 0$. Thus, we have now for r the limitation

$$(5.13) \qquad 0 < r < R.$$

It follows from the definitions (5.11) and (5.12), that r is the length of the vector joining the origin to the point (ξ_1, ξ_2). In consequence,

$$(5.14) \qquad \xi_1^2 + \xi_2^2 = r^2.$$

Applying the second formula of (5.3) we obtain

$$(5.15) \qquad f(x_1, x_2) - f(x_1^0, x_2^0) =$$
$$r\left\{ f_1^0 p_1 + f_2^0 p_2 + \frac{r}{2}[f_{11}^\theta p_1^2 + 2f_{12}^\theta p_1 p_2 + f_{22}^\theta p_2^2] \right\}.$$

Let us suppose that the absolute values of the second derivatives f_{ij}^θ have an upper bound M_R when the point is situated, inside the circle of radius R. Moreover we suppose that M_R is finite. Then, the absolute values of the expression inside the square brackets in (5.15) will be at most equal to

$$(5.16) \qquad \frac{R}{2} M_R \cdot (|p_1| + |p_2|)^2.$$

By taking R sufficiently small, we can reduce this value at will. If now at least one of the first order partial derivatives is effectively positive at the point (x_1^0, x_2^0) – for example, if f_1^0 is equal to a strictly positive number c – it is certain that we can find in the circle of radius R points which make the whole right-hand side of the formula (5.15) *positive*. In fact, we can, for example, choose: $p_2 = 0$ and $p_1 = 1$, after having chosen the radius R in such a way, that the absolute value of the expression (5.16) becomes *less* than the strictly positive number c. The point (x_1^0, x_2^0) in this case cannot be a maximum for the function f. This proves that a necessary condition for the function f to have a maximum is that the partial derivative f_1^0 should be zero. In the same way it is easy to see that the partial derivative f_2^0 also must be zero at such a point.

The situation is the same for a minimum of the function f.

In a completely general way, it is proved now that at each point which is an extremum for a function f satisfying the conditions which are required for f to have an expansion of the form given by the second formula of (5.3) – in other words, a function having a second derivative –, the two partial derivatives f_1^0 and f_2^0 must necessarily be equal to zero (when the domain of definition of f is considered as an open space, i.e., when its boundary points are excluded).

The generalisation of Taylor's formula for the case of n variables. The necessary conditions of the first order in the case of n variables

This reasoning can easily be extended to the case of n variables, $x_1, x_2, \ldots, x_n$. The Taylor expansion for a function of n variables is

$$
\begin{aligned}
f(x_1, x_2, \ldots x_n) = f^0 &+ \sum_{i=1}^{n} f_i^0 \xi_i + \frac{1}{2!} \sum_{i=1}^{n} \sum_{j=1}^{n} f_{ij}^0 \xi_i \xi_j \\
&+ \cdots + \frac{1}{(v-1)!} \sum_{i=1}^{n} \sum_{j=1}^{n} \cdots \sum_{h=1}^{n} f_{ij\ldots h}^0 \xi_i \xi_j \cdots \xi_h \\
&+ \frac{1}{v!} \sum_{i=1}^{n} \sum_{j=1}^{n} \cdots \sum_{h=1}^{n} \sum_{k=1}^{n} f_{ij\ldots hk}^\theta \xi_i \xi_j \cdots \xi_h \xi_k
\end{aligned}
$$

(5.17)

33

where

(5.18) $\xi_i = x_i - x_i^0$ $(i = 1, 2, \dots n)$,

and where $i, j, \dots, h$ are $(v-1)$ summation indices, and $i, j, \dots, h, k, v$ summation indices $(v = 1, 2, \dots)$.

The arguments of the derivatives on the right-hand side of (5.17) are everywhere $(x_1^0, x_2^0, \dots, x_n^0)$, except for the last term – i.e. the v-th sum –, where they are

(5.19) $x_i^0 + \theta(x_i - x_i^0)$ $(i = 1, 2, \dots n)$,

θ being bounded by (5.6).

The condition for the validity of expansion (5.17) is that all the vth derivatives should be continuous in the domain under consideration. Applying this expansion for $v = 2$, we obtain the following theorem:

THEOREM (5.20). Let $f(x_1, x_2, \dots, x_n)$ be a function of n variables, having continuous second derivatives around a point $(x_1^0, x_2^0, \dots, x_n^0)$, which is not a boundary point of the domain of definition of the function; a necessary condition for the point $(x_1^0, x_2^0, \dots, x_n^0)$ to be a local extremum for the function is that all partial derivatives of the first order of the function should vanish at this point.

Further remarks concerning the coordinates of points situated on the segment joining the two points (x_1^0, x_2^0) and (x_1, x_2)

The importance of (5.5–6) is that when (5.6) is satisfied, the coordinates (5.5) give a point on the segment joining the points (x_1^0, x_2^0) and (x_1, x_2). We put

$$x_1' = x_1^0 + \theta(x_1 - x_1^0) \qquad x_2' = x_2^0 + \theta(x_2 - x_2^0).$$

When θ varies from 0 to 1, the variable point (x_1', x_2') will vary from (x_1^0, x_2^0) to (x_1, x_2) in the same monotonic way as x_1' varies from x_1^0 to x_1 and as x_2' varies from x_2^0 to x_2. That the variation acts along the segment joining (x_1^0, x_2^0) and (x_1, x_2) points to the fact that every point (x_1', x_2') which results from assigning a definite value to θ in the above mentioned formulae will satisfy the equation of the straight line joining the points (x_1^0, x_2^0) and (x_1, x_2). One can easily verify that this is in fact the case, by

34

taking an arbitrary value of θ and substituting the corresponding (x'_1, x'_2) into the equation of this straight line, which is

$$x'_2 = x^0_2 + \frac{x_2 - x^0_2}{x_1 - x^0_1}(x'_1 - x^0_1).$$

Further geometric remarks concerning the coordinates of the points situated inside a circle of radius R

Let us illustrate in a more precise way the choice of the neighbourhood of (x^0_1, x^0_2) according to (5.11–16).

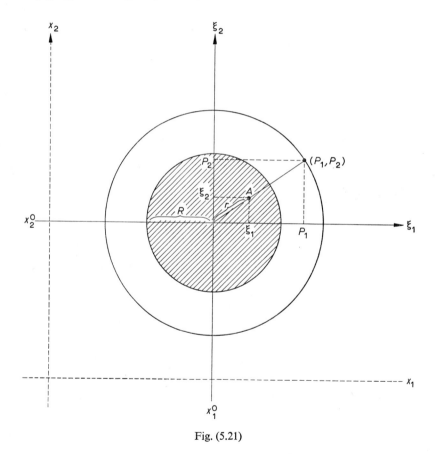

Fig. (5.21)

In figure (5.21) the dotted lines at the bottom and on the left represent the axes of the coordinate system x_1, x_2, and the solid lines the axes of the coordinate system ξ_1, ξ_2. The relation between the x-s and the ξ-s is as given by the last line of (5.3), that is $\xi_1 = x_1 - x_1^0$, $\xi_2 = x_2 - x_2^0$.

In the figure, the outer circle is the unit circle, i.e. the circle with radius 1, having the point (x_1^0, x_2^0) as centre. The disc bounded by the inner circle (of radius R) is the chosen neighbourhood. We see from the figure how every point situated inside this neighbourhood – for example the point A – can be defined by the numbers p_1 and p_2, coordinates of a point situated on the unit circle, and by the distance r between the origin (of the coordinate system ξ) and the point A. The numbers p_1 and p_2 are, respectively, the cosine and the sine of the angle formed by the vector pointing from the origin to the point A and the positive axis ξ_1.

For every point of the domain contained within the circle of radius R – i.e. for every set of numbers p_1, p_2, r such that (p_1, p_2) is situated on the unit circle and $r < R$ –, we can calculate the value of f and compare it with the value f^0 at the point $\xi_1 = 0$, $\xi_2 = 0$ (i.e. at the point $x_1 = x_1^0$, $x_2 = x_2^0$). The question now is whether it is possible to choose a sufficiently small R such that for every point inside the circle of radius R (except (x_1^0, x_2^0)), we have $f < f^0$ (f thus exhibiting a maximum at the point (x_1^0, x_2^0)), or that for every point situated inside the circle of radius R (except (x_1^0, x_2^0)), we have $f > f^0$ (f thus exhibiting a minimum at (x_1^0, x_2^0)). These are the conditions of the two cases discussed in (5.15–16).

EXAMPLES

As examples to this chapter, the reader should refer to the beginning of the following examples:

Example (10.1′) (p. 113) up to and excluding "For each of these two extrema..."

Example (10.2′) (p. 116) up to and excluding "Let us examine this point more closely..."

Example (11.1′) (p. 120), up to and excluding "The matrix of the second-order derivatives..."

THE NECESSARY CONDITION OF THE FIRST ORDER IN THE CASE OF TWO OR MORE VARIABLES WITH CONSTRAINTS

Intuitive representation and graphical illustration of a constraint

At first we explore the situation with the help of a graphical representation Let $f(x_1, x_2)$ be a function of two variables – for example, a function whose level curves are of the form (5.1) (T marking a summit and not a depression of the "terrain"). If we wish to find the maximum of the function *without imposing any constraint* on the variables x_1, x_2, we reach the point T in the way indicated in Chapter 5.

We now suppose that the variables are subjected to a constraint in the form of an equation.

(6.1) $$C(x_1, x_2) = 0$$

Graphically this condition will be expressed as a curve – for example, the dotted curve AB in figure (6.2). The imposed constraint is now that we cannot move freely in the (x_1, x_2) plane, but only *along this curve*. To search for the maximum of the function $f(x_1, x_2)$ subject to constraint (6.1) means to look for the greatest value of $f(x_1, x_2)$ – in other words, the highest level curve – which we can attain by moving along the curve AB.

It is intuitively clear that we shall find this if we move along the curve AB until we arrive at a point W, where we have *tangency* between the curve AB and a level curve, i.e. where the gradient of the function $f(x_1, x_2)$ is collinear with the normal vector to the curve representing the condition (note in the figure the arrow starting at W). In fact, if we place ourselves to the south-east of W, for example at one of the points R or S, then, by moving along the curve AB we can reach a higher level curve of the function f. The situation is the same if we place ourselves to the north-west of W, for example at one of the points P or Q. Once we have reached the point of tangency W, we cannot go higher.

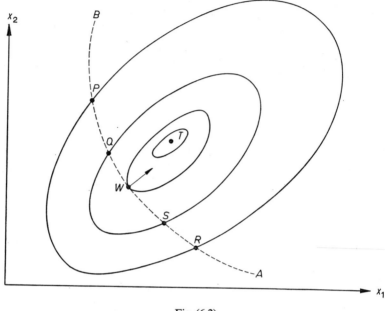

Fig. (6.2)

The terminology associated with 'terrain' and 'path'

Let us represent the curve AB as "a path through the terrain" and follow it. We start by "climbing the slope", passing through the points R and S, and having passed through the highest point of the route at W, we shall "descend" through the points Q and P (cf. the analogous problems in the theory of production).

The direct formulation of the condition of the first order

The normal of the curve AB is an arrow whose components are proportional to the partial derivatives of the function C, i.e. proportional to

$$(6.3) \qquad C_1 = \frac{\partial C(x_1, x_2)}{\partial x_1} \quad \text{and} \quad C_2 = \frac{\partial C(x_1, x_2)}{\partial x_2}.$$

The simplest way to convince ourselves of this is to imagine that we have drawn the level curves of the function C as we have done for the function *f*. Just as the normal of the level curves of *f* has the components f_1 and f_2, the normal of the level curves of C will have the components C_1 and C_2. And the meaning of equation (6.1) is simply that among the level curves of the function C we have chosen a particular curve, on which the constant value of C is zero.

To say that the two normal vectors are oriented in the same direction is to say that the numbers f_1 and f_2 are proportional to the numbers C_1 and C_2, i.e. that

(6.4)
$$\frac{f_1}{C_1} = \frac{f_2}{C_2}.$$

This equality, jointly with (6.1), furnishes two relations between the two variables x_1 and x_2. Depending on the case, these may determine one or more pairs of numbers (x_1, x_2) which satisfy them, or none. It is easy to see that the condition (6.4) is just as much valid for a minimum as for a maximum. Thus, generally, (6.4) is a necessary condition for an extremum.

Formulation of the first-order condition by means of a Lagrange multiplier

The condition for tangency (6.4) can also be expressed in another way. We say that the numbers f_1 and f_2 can be obtained by multiplying C_1 and C_2 by a common factor λ, which is for the time being non-specified. We thus have

(6.5)
$$f_1 + \lambda C_1 = 0 \quad \text{and} \quad f_2 + \lambda C_2 = 0.$$

It is clear that if (6.4) is satisfied, we shall also have (6.5), because λ represents the same number in both the first and second expression of (6.5). Conversely, if we have (6.5) we must have (6.4). The value of the common factor λ is undetermined only if we imagine that we only have the equality (6.4) alone, or the equations (6.5) alone. It does not matter much in fact whether we claim to have established the equality (6.4) between the two variables x_1 and x_2 or whether we assert that we only consider the two equations (6.5) between the three variables x_1, x_2 and λ: it is evident that in both cases the problem has one degree of freedom. But if we add (6.1), λ becomes determined. Thus we can say either that we have two equations (6.1) and (6.4) between the two variables x_1 and x_2, or that we have three equations (6.1) and (6.5) between the three variables x_1, x_2 and λ. We shall give preference to the second formulation.

In this form we can say that a necessary condition for the function $f(x_1, x_2)$ to have an extremum subject to (6.1) is that we should have (6.5), λ being an auxiliary parameter, which takes a definite value if in addition to the conditions for tangency (6.5), (6.1) is also taken into account.

This formulation can be written in the following form, which is not without interest:

We consider the function

(6.6) $$\Phi(x_1, x_2) = f(x_1, x_2) + \lambda C(x_1, x_2)$$

where λ is a value undetermined for the time being. We apply the necessary condition of the first order for the extremum of the function Φ when x_1 and x_2 are considered as independent variables without any constraint and λ is a constant. Next, we determine the value λ by introducing the constraint (6.1).

To carry out the operation indicated above, we use (5.20) and put:

(6.7) $$\Phi_1 = 0 \quad \text{and} \quad \Phi_2 = 0,$$

where

(6.8) $$\Phi_i = \frac{\partial \Phi(x_1, x_2)}{\partial x_1} \qquad (i = 1, 2).$$

When λ is considered as a constant, the conditions (6.7) are equivalent to (6.5). The nature of the condition (6.1) is not modified by the formulation of the problem which we adopt here.

The provisionally undetermined constant λ which we have introduced in the construction (6.6) is called a *Lagrange multiplier*.

Definition of m constraints

This reasoning can be easily generalised and extended to the case when one looks for the maximum of a function $f(x_1, x_2, \cdots, x_n)$ of n variables subject to $m (\leqslant n)$ constraints

(6.9)
$$
\begin{aligned}
C_1(x_1, x_2, \ldots x_n) &= 0 \\
C_2(x_1, x_2, \ldots x_n) &= 0 \\
&\cdots\cdots\cdots\cdots\cdots \\
C_m(x_1, x_2, \ldots x_n) &= 0
\end{aligned}
$$

We put

$$(6.10) \qquad C_{hi} = \frac{\partial C_h(x_1, x_2, \ldots x_n)}{\partial x_i} \qquad \begin{array}{l} h = 1, 2, \ldots m \\ i = 1, 2, \ldots n \end{array}$$

We consider a point $(x_1^0, x_2^0, \ldots, x_n^0)$ around which the matrix*

$$(6.11) \qquad \begin{Vmatrix} C_{11} & C_{12} & \ldots & C_{1n} \\ C_{21} & C_{22} & \ldots & C_{2n} \\ \cdots\cdots\cdots\cdots\cdots\cdots \\ C_{m1} & C_{m2} & \ldots & C_{mn} \end{Vmatrix}$$

is of rank m. In other words, there is in this matrix at least one non-vanishing determinant of order $(m \times m)$. Without restricting the generality we can suppose that the determinant formed from the last m columns is different from zero, which we express by

$$(6.12) \qquad \begin{vmatrix} C_{1,n-m+1} & C_{1,n-m+2} & \ldots & C_{1n} \\ C_{2,n-m+1} & C_{2,n-m+2} & \ldots & C_{2n} \\ \cdots\cdots\cdots\cdots\cdots\cdots\cdots\cdots\cdots \\ C_{m,n-m+1} & C_{m,n-m+2} & \ldots & C_{mn} \end{vmatrix} \neq 0.$$

Direct formulation of the first-order conditions in the case of n variables with m constraints

We can now consider the m variables $x_{n-m+1}, x_{n-m+2}, \ldots, x_n$ – around the point $(x_1^0, x_2^0, \ldots, x_n^0)$ – as functions of the first $n-m$ variables $x_1, x_2, \ldots, x_{n-m}$, and we imagine that the system (6.9) is solved with respect to $x_{n-m+1}, x_{n-m+2}, \ldots, x_n$. We can further imagine that these expressions are substituted into $f(x_1, x_2, \ldots, x_n)$ and, finally, that we wish to find the extrema of this function with respect to $x_1, x_2, \ldots, x_{n-m}$, which from now must be considered as $(n-m)$ independent variables. In this way we must, in virtue of (5.20), impose, as necessary conditions for an extremum, the following conditions:

$$(6.13) \qquad f_i + \sum_{k=n-m+1}^{n} f_k \frac{\partial x_k}{\partial x_i} = 0 \qquad (i = 1, 2, \ldots (n - m)).$$

* See Chapters IX and XIII for the concepts and properties of linear equations, matrices, and determinants which are used here.

For a given i, (6.13) contains the m derivatives $\partial x_k/\partial x_i$ ($k=n-m+1$, $n-m+2$, ..., n). These can be determined by means of the following system of linear equations, which is obtained by differentiating (6.9) with respect to x_i

(6.14)
$$C_{hi} + \sum_{k=n-m+1}^{n} C_{hk}\frac{\partial x_k}{\partial x_i} = 0 \qquad \begin{array}{l} h = 1, 2, \ldots m \\ i = 1, 2, \ldots (n-m) \end{array}$$

In view of (6.12) this system of linear equations certainly has a solution with respect to the m values $\partial x_k/\partial x_i$ ($k=n-m+1$, ..., n) (cf. Chapter VIII). If we construct a linear form – e.g. the linear form (6.13) – out of these m values, we can write

$$\sum_{k=n-m+1}^{n} f_k \frac{\partial x_k}{\partial x_i} =$$

(6.15)

$$\begin{vmatrix} 0 & f_{n-m+1} & f_{n-m+2} & \cdots f_n \\ C_{1i} & C_{1,n-m+1} & C_{1,n-m+2} & \cdots C_{1,n} \\ C_{2i} & C_{2,n-m+1} & C_{2,n-m+2} & \cdots C_{2,n} \\ \cdots\cdots\cdots\cdots\cdots\cdots\cdots\cdots \\ C_{mi} & C_{m,n-m+1} & C_{m,n-m+2} & \cdots C_{m,n} \end{vmatrix} : |C|$$

where $|C|$ is the determinant of (6.12). Consequently, the system (6.13) can be written as

$$\begin{vmatrix} 0 & f_{n-m+1} & \cdots f_n \\ C_{1i} & C_{1,n-m+1} & \cdots C_{1,n} \\ \cdots\cdots\cdots\cdots\cdots\cdots \\ C_{mi} & C_{m,n-m+1} & \cdots C_{m,n} \end{vmatrix} = -f_i|C|$$

which can be rewritten as

(6.16)
$$\begin{vmatrix} f_i & f_{n-m+1} & f_{n-m+2} & \cdots f_n \\ C_{1i} & C_{1,n-m+1} & C_{1,n-m+2} & \cdots C_{1,n} \\ C_{2i} & C_{2,n-m+1} & C_{2,n-m+2} & \cdots C_{2,n} \\ \cdots\cdots\cdots\cdots\cdots\cdots\cdots\cdots \\ C_{mi} & C_{m,n-m+1} & C_{m,n-m+2} & \cdots C_{m,n} \end{vmatrix} = 0$$

$$\left(i = 1, 2, \ldots (n-m)\right)$$

42

Here we have $(n-m)$ equations which, together with the "m" equations (6.9), determine the n values $x_1, x_2, ..., x_n$. Thus – assuming that (6.12) holds – a necessary condition for an extremum of $f(x_1, x_2, ..., x_n)$ under the condition (6.9) is that the $(n-m)$ equations of (6.16) and the m equations of (6.9) should be simultaneously satisfied.

Formulation by means of Lagrange multipliers

We can formulate the condition in another way, which is stronger (at least *a priori*) than (6.16). The more exacting a necessary condition is, the more powerful it is. (Clearly the ideal would be to be able to state a necessary condition *so exacting* that it also becomes sufficient.) We will show that at a point which is an extremum for $f(x_1, x_2, ..., x_n)$ under the condition (6.9), there exist m numbers $\lambda_1, \lambda_2, ..., \lambda_m$ with the property:

$$(6.17) \qquad f_i + \sum_{h=1}^{m} \lambda_h C_{hi} = 0 \qquad (i = 1, 2, ... n)$$

When such numbers exist, (6.16) must be necessarily fulfilled. In fact, if we multiply the second line of (6.16) by λ_1, the third by λ_2, etc., and add all that to the first line, we obtain there zeros throughout. Thus, the condition which we have stated above is – at least *a priori* – more exacting than (6.16).

To prove the existence of the m numbers $\lambda_1, \lambda_2, ..., \lambda_m$, with the property that (6.17) is satisfied for the set of n indices: $i=1, 2, ..., n$, we begin by determining the m numbers $\lambda_1, \lambda_2, ..., \lambda_m$ in such a way that (6.17) should be satisfied for the m indices $i=n-m+1, n-m+2, ..., n$. This is always possible, in virtue of (6.12). We will show that these m numbers will then satisfy (6.17) also for the remaining $(n-m)$ indices: $i=1, 2, ..., n-m$.

At a point which is an extremum for $f(x_1, x_2, ..., x_n)$ subject to (6.9), (6.13) and (6.14) are always satisfied. We multiply (6.14) by the number λ_h determined above, and sum with respect to h. To the sum we add (6.13). Hence

$$(6.18) \qquad f_i + \sum_{h=1}^{m} \lambda_h C_{hi} + \sum_{k=n-m+1}^{n} \left[f_k + \sum_{h=1}^{m} \lambda_h C_{hk} \right] \frac{\partial x_k}{\partial x_i} = 0$$
$$(i = 1, 2, ... (n - m)).$$

By definition, the numbers λ_1, λ_2, ..., λ_m satisfy (6.17) for $i=n-m+1$, $n-m+2$, ..., n. Hence the brackets in (6.18) will vanish for $k=n-m+1$, $n-m+2$, ..., n. The equation (6.18) will thus reduce to

$$(6.19) \qquad f_i + \sum_{h=1}^{m} \lambda_h C_{hi} = 0 \qquad (i = 1, 2, \dots (n-m)).$$

This means that the numbers λ_1, λ_2, ..., λ_m under consideration are such that (6.17) is satisfied for the set of n indices $i=1, 2, ..., n$.

We see that the n equations (6.17) can be established in a purely formal way by constructing, with the help of the n provisionally undetermined numbers λ_1, λ_2, ..., λ_m, the function

$$(6.20) \qquad \Phi(x_1, x_2, \dots x_n) = f(x_1, x_2, \dots x_n) + \sum_{h=1}^{m} \lambda_h C_h(x_1, x_2, \dots x_n)$$

and imposing the necessary condition of the first order for an extremum of the function $\Phi(x_1, x_2, ..., x_n)$, when $x_1, x_2, ..., x_n$ are considered as n independent variables without constraints, and $\lambda_1, \lambda_2, ..., \lambda_m$ as m constants.

In this way one obtains n equations which together with the m equations (6.9) determine the $(n+m)$ values $x_1, x_2, ..., x_n$ and $\lambda_1, \lambda_2, ..., \lambda_m$.

The values $\lambda_1, \lambda_2, ..., \lambda_m$ are called Lagrange multipliers (in the general case with m conditions).

The method of Lagrange multipliers is well adapted to many theoretical problems. On the other hand, if it is a question of writing down the necessary conditions explicitly, (6.16) – which is obtained from (6.17) by elimination of the λ's – is preferable.

SUPPLEMENT

It is interesting to see intuitively, but without rigour, how one can introduce the Lagrange multipliers directly. Their theoretical significance thus will become clearer.

We shall restrict our reasoning to the case when we wish to find the extrema of a function $f(x_1, x_2)$ of two variables, subject to the condition that x_1 and x_2 have to satisfy the equation:

$$(6.1) \qquad C(x_1, x_2) = 0$$

Let us extend the problem a little by investigating – as a function of the parameter ε, which takes values in a small neighbourhood of zero – the extrema of f when the equation between x_1 and x_2 is

(6.1′)
$$C\ (x_1, x_2) = \varepsilon$$

This reduces to (6.1) for $\varepsilon = 0$.

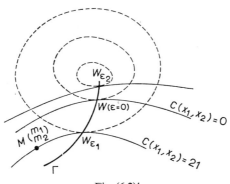

Fig. (6.2)′

We shall be able to use the intuitive figure 6.2′ again, provided that this time we also draw the system of curves defined by (6.1′). For each value of ε we determine $W_{(\varepsilon)}$, the point where (6.1′) has a common tangent with a level curve of $f(x_1, x_2)$. When ε varies, we obtain in this way a curve as a locus of these points of tangency. Let $\Gamma_{(\varepsilon)}$ be this curve. $\Gamma_{(\varepsilon)}$ evidently passes through the point W, already found, corresponding to $\varepsilon = 0$, whose coordinates are x_1^0, x_2^0. It is clear that if $W(\varepsilon = 0)$ is an extremum for the function $f(x_1, x_2)$ along the curve Γ only, W will be a local stationary point of f in a small area surrounding W.

In fact, let us take a point M with coordinates m_1, m_2 near W. Through M will pass the curve $C(x_1, x_2) = C(m_1, m_2)$ which will intersect Γ in the point W_{ε_1}. At this point W_{ε_1}, f is extremal by the definition of Γ_ε, or more generally its value will differ very little from the value at M, even if $\overset{\frown}{W_{\varepsilon_1}M}$ is not negligible. And since at W_{ε_1}, f is stationary along Γ, the value of f at W differs very little from its value at W_{ε_1} and M, even if $\overset{\frown}{WM}$ is not negligible. f is thus truly stationary at W.

However, in general, there is no reason whatever why f should be stationary at W along Γ. But if we consider the function

$$\Phi = f(x_1, x_2) + \lambda C\ (x_1, x_2)$$

along Γ, it is clear that one can determine λ in such a way that $f + \lambda C$ should have an extremum at W along Γ. In fact, one can imagine that the coordinates of the different points W, W_{ε_1}, etc., along Γ have been expressed as functions of a parameter t. Φ becomes the sum function of the two functions $\bar{f}(t)$ and $\lambda\bar{C}(t)$. If $t = 0$ is the value of the parameter at W, Φ, a function of a single variable, will have an extremum at W if the derivative $f'(0) + \lambda C'(0)$ is zero. From this, in general, one can determine $\lambda = \bar{f}'(0)/\bar{C}'(0)$.

Our reasoning would be much simpler, and much more attractive, if we could assert that W is a maximum along Γ, as it is, for example, along $C(x_1, x_2) = 0$. But our reasoning only shows that in general W is a maximum, or a minimum. If W were a maximum along Γ, $f + \lambda C$ would clearly have a local maximum at W. But, as one can see from Chapter V, it is just as likely that W will be in fact a minimum for $\bar{f}(t) + \lambda\bar{C}(t)$ along Γ. And the only conclusion one can establish is that there exists a value λ, such that if f is an extremal for $C(x_1, x_2) = 0$, then $f(x_1, x_2) + \lambda C(x_1, x_2)$ is stationary (but not necessarily extremal).

REMARKS

1. On page 40 we read: "Next, we determine the value of λ by introducing the constraint (6.1)". Naturally, the idea here is not that one must necessarily *solve* the equations in a fixed order, but only that "besides, we must taken into consideration..." The equations obtained by putting the partial derivatives of Φ with respect to x_1 and x_2 equal to zero – that is, the equations (6.5) – and also the constraint (6.1) give rise to a system which determines the three values x_1, x_2 and λ simultaneously. As for knowing whether one can eliminate one of these quantities by examining the system of equations only for the other quantities, this is a practical question which one has to decide in each given case.

(2). The reasoning which leads to (6.20) can be summed up briefly as follows:

At a point which is an extremum for the function $f(x_1, ..., x_n)$ subject to (6.9), it is *necessary*, if (6.12) is assumed, that (6.13) and (6.14) should be satisfied.

When these conditions are fulfilled, there must exist m numbers $\lambda_1, \lambda_2, ..., \lambda_m$ such that (6.17) is satisfied for every $i = 1, 2, ..., n$.

If we apply the following algorithm: to construct the function (6.20) where $\lambda_1, \lambda_2, ..., \lambda_m$ are m constants undetermined for the time being (and thus independent of $x_1 ... x_n$) and to impose on Φ the necessary condition of the first order for an extremum (the variables $x_1 ... x_n$ being considered as independent variables, and $\lambda_1 ... \lambda_m$ as constants), we arrive at (6.17); in other words, by constructing the function (6.20) and applying this algorithm to it, we obtain a set of *necessary* conditions for the function f to have a *conditional* extremum (with respect to (6.9)).

46

CHAPTER VI

EXAMPLES

As examples to this chapter, the reader should refer to the beginning of the following examples:

Example 12.1' (p. 136) up to and excluding "Let us put now..."

Example 12.2' (p. 138) up to and excluding "We put now $x_1 = x_1{}^0 + \Delta x_1$..."

Example 12.3' (p. 140) up to and excluding "Taking the values of C_{ij} into..."

SIMULTANEOUS SEARCH FOR
THE EXTREMA OF SEVERAL FUNCTIONS.
PARETO OPTIMALITY

Occasionally one comes across problems involving *several* functions

$$(7.1) \qquad f_1(x_1 \ldots x_n), \quad f_2(x_1 \ldots x_n) \ldots f_N(x_1 \ldots x_n)$$

which one wishes to make simultaneously "as large as possible". Clearly such a problem is not well defined. In most cases only by giving up control of one of the functions can one increase another one, and *vice versa*.

There are two different ways of making this problem more specific. One method is to introduce a *composite function*

$$(7.2) \qquad \Omega(f_1, f_2, \ldots, f_N),$$

i.e. a function of the variables $f_1, f_2, \ldots, f_N$, given in an explicit form; and to search for the *maximum* of Ω. If, for each function $f_1, f_2, \ldots, f_N$ of (7.2) we substitute their appropriate expressions as functions of $x_1, x_2, \ldots, x_n$, we make Ω also a function of $x_1, x_2, \ldots, x_n$, and we have again the usual maximum problem.

It might happen – and that is now a special case – that Ω is a *linear* function

$$(7.3) \qquad \Omega(f_1, f_2, \ldots f_N) = w_1 f_1 + w_2 f_2 + \cdots + w_N f_N.$$

The peculiar fact here is that because of the nature of the problem we are in the position – or can find ourselves obliged – to determine the *weights* $w_1, w_2, \ldots, w_N$, according to how we assess the relative importance of the different functions $f_1, f_2, \ldots, f_N$. There are many economic problems which can be stated in these terms. For example, *given prices* can be taken for the weights $w_1, w_2, \ldots, w_N$.

Abandonment of the investigation of a composite function. Definition of the Pareto optimality

The other approach to the problem is to give up the construction of a composite function, and to confine ourselves to stating what can be said without introducing an Ω. Even in this general formulation, we can say *something* important concerning the problem. In fact, it is clear that, if each of the functions is such that we wish to increase it (if we can do so) without doing this at the expense of any other function, then we can exclude as *non-desirable* a whole category of points $(x_1, x_2, ..., x_n)$: one eliminates all points $x=(x_1, x_2, ..., x_n)$ such that by passing from x to another point $x' =(x'_1, x'_2, ..., x'_n)$ none of the functions $f_1, f_2, ..., f_N$ diminishes, and at least one of them effectively increases. Thus we have found at least a *necessary* criterion, which our point x must satisfy: it must be such that there does not exist another point x' having the property stated above. A point x satisfying this requirement is said to be a *Pareto-optimal point* (after the Italian economist and mathematician Vilfredo Pareto). In exact terms, we can state this definition in the following form.

DEFINITION (7.4). A point $x=(x_1, x_2, ..., x_n)$ is said to be a Pareto-optimal point when – within the limits of the domain of variation considered – *there exists no point* $x' =(x'_1, x'_2, ..., x'_n)$ which would have the property that on passing from x to x' the functions $f_1 (x_1, ..., x_n)$, $f_2 (x_1, ..., x_n)$, ... $f_N (x_1, ..., x_n)$ do not decrease, and at least one of them effectively increases.

Analysing the notion of Pareto optimality, it is easy to see that one can distinguish between optimality in the global and in the local sense, and between strong optimality and weak optimality (when we assume the condition that at least one of the functions $f_1, ..., f_N$ must be effectively increased). Finally, we can consider Pareto optimality with and without constraints. All these considerations can be derived by arguments identical to those which we have employed above in connection with the extrema of a single function.

Constrained Pareto optimality

The constrained Pareto optimality assumes a particular importance. For the sake of clarity we shall state the definition in its entirety.

DEFINITION (7.5). A point $x = (x_1, x_2, ..., x_n)$ is said to be Pareto-optimal subject to the constraint C, when in the first place x satisfies C, and in the second place, there exists no other point $x' = (x'_1, x'_2, ..., x'_n)$ satisfying C and such that by passing from x to x' the functions $f_1(x_1 ... x_n), f_2(x_1 ... x_n), ..., f_N(x_1 ... x_n)$ do not decrease and at least one of them effectively increases.

The set of points which are optimal according to the definition (7.5) can be denoted by the symbol:

$$(7.6) \qquad\qquad Par\,[C].$$

The constraints C can be expressed by means of equations or inequalities satisfied by the variables $x_1, x_2, ..., x_n$, or by various other means.

In general, there is not one point alone but a whole set of points which will have the property of Pareto optimality in the presence of a given type of constraints.

The number of elements of this set can be greater or smaller. In this respect, one must take notice of a circumstance which, at first sight, is very surprising, and seems contrary to common sense.

Let us consider two different kinds of constraints: a constraint c, of the *weak* type, and another constraint C, of the *strong* type. To say that c is a weak and C a strong constraint means that if we take an arbitrary point $(x_1, x_2, ..., x_n)$ and find that it satisfies C then we can be certain that it also satisfies c, without being able to assert the converse.

Having defined the concept of "weak" and "strong" in this way, it is easy to show that the part of the space $(x_1, x_2, ..., x_n)$ which satisfies C is contained in the part of the space which satisfies c. In other words, more concisely: the part of the space which satisfies a constraint diminishes when the constraint is strengthened.

When it is the question of the Pareto optimality, the situation is, in a sense, the reverse: if we confine ourselves to considering the part of the space which satisfies C, we find that the class of points which are Pareto optimal under the weak constraint c is contained in the class of those which are Pareto optimal under the strong constraint C, without the converse being true. As a general rule, the class of points Pareto optimal under the stronger constraint C is effectively more numerous than that of the points Pareto optimal under the weaker constraint c; in other words in the part of the space which satisfies C one can find points which are Pareto optimal under the constraint C, but *not* under the constraint c.

We can represent this peculiarity schematically in the form of a diagram (figure 7.7). The points which satisfy c are placed inside the curve $\rightarrow c$,

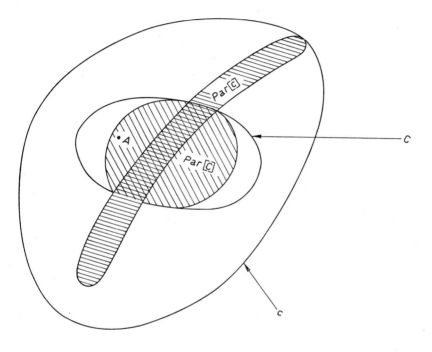

Fig. (7.7)

and the points which satisfy C inside the curve $\rightarrow C$. The region of the points Par [C] is striped, that of the points Par [c] which satisfy C, is shaded. One observes that the point A is Par [C], but not Par [c].

Various applications of the notion of Pareto optimality, notably in the theory of production

In economics, one comes across many problems which are amenable to a formulation inspired by the notion of Pareto optimality. This is true not only in the case treated originally by the author, where $f_1, f_2, ..., f_N$ are

51

preference functions relating to individual consumers, but also in many other cases, where the functions assume quite different meanings. In this respect, the theory of production furnishes an interesting example. Let $f_1(x_1, ..., x_n)$ be the quantity produced by means of the factors of production $x_1, ..., x_n$, and let $f_2(x_1, ..., x_n)$ be the total cost of the production in a given system of prices. As for the question of optimality, it is evident that one would not stop at a point such that one can reach a stage beyond it where the quantity of the product will be greater without the cost of production being greater, or such that the cost of production will be smaller without the quantity produced being smaller. If we use the language of the theory of production, we will find in this example an illustration of the principle of *the in every respect economic substitution* which leads to the definition of the substitumal. This now appears, in this case, as being a solution of a problem of Pareto optimality.

A more detailed discussion on the concept of optimality in the sense of Pareto, – notably in the presence of constraints, – will be found in the paper entitled 'On Welfare Theory and Pareto Regions', presented by Ragnar Frisch at the Rome meeting of the International Association for Research in Income and Wealth, in September, 1953.

EXAMPLES

EXAMPLE (7.1)

We are going first to study an example of the classical Pareto optimum problem (in particular, in the theory of international commerce and trade) geometrically.

Let us consider two goods ξ and η, and suppose that two individuals I_1 and I_2 possess quantities x_1 and y_1, and x_2 and y_2 respectively of these goods. Let us put:

$$x_1 + x_2 = X \qquad y_1 + y_2 = Y.$$

We assume that the satisfaction obtained by the two individuals from the possession of these quantities is measurable by the product of the two numbers measuring these quantities. Thus with the notations of the text we have:

$$f_1(x_1, y_1) = x_1 y_1$$
$$f_2(x_2, y_2) = x_2 y_2$$

Under these conditions one can ask whether it is possible for the two individuals to augment their respective satisfactions simultaneously by exchanging a quantity of ξ for a quantity of η.

In this exchange, the total quantities of the two goods always remain equal to X

and Y respectively. Now in this particular case one can conceive a simultaneous graphical representation of the two domains of satisfaction: For the first individual we take any two ordinary rectangular coordinate axes O_1x_1, O_1y_1. For the second individual we take on the same diagram two axes O_2x_2 and O_2y_2, which are parallel to O_1x_1 and O_1y_1 respectively, but in the opposite direction, the coordinates of O_2 with respect to $x_1O_1y_1$ being X and Y.

Whatever are now the quantities exchanged, we find under these conditions, that if $M(x_1 + \delta\xi, y_1 + \delta\eta)$ is the point representing the goods of I_1, after the exchange of the quantities $\delta\xi$ and $\delta\eta$, the same point M will have in the system $x_2O_2y_2$ the coordinates $X - x_1 - \delta\xi$, $Y - y_1 - \delta\eta$, that is $x_2 - \delta\xi$, $y_2 - \delta\eta$. Thus the same point M will represent in the system $x_2O_2y_2$ the goods of I_2 after the exchange. Moreover, since the quantities of the goods are positive, all the possible points M will be in the rectangle R whose opposite vertices are O_1 and O_2, and whose sides are on the coordinate axes.

Let us draw now the equilateral hyperbolae (drawn as solid curves in $x_1O_1y_1$, and as dotted curves in $x_2O_2y_2$) representing the curves of equal satisfaction for I_1 and I_2. One obtains in this way two interlocking systems of curves. On each system the satisfaction increases gradually as one moves away from the respective origins.

Let us now consider the initial point M and consider the curves C_1 and C_2 relative to I_1 and I_2 which pass through this point. Using simple geometric properties, which we ask the reader to accept (or to prove himself) and which are in any case obvious from the diagram, we can assert that if M is not on the diagonal O_1O_2, C_1 and C_2 will intersect, and delimit an area A bounded by two arcs MM' on C_1 and C_2, M' being obliquely symmetrical to M with respect to O_1O_2 and following the direction of the second diagonal of the rectangle R. We have shaded this area A on the diagram (7.1'). It is clear that A is the locus of points of R where the satisfactions of I_1 and I_2 can be simultaneously augmented. On the outside of A, in the dotted region opposite to A with respect to the vertices M and M', the two satisfactions would diminish. In the rest of R, for the region marked with crosses, one can augment the satisfaction of I_1

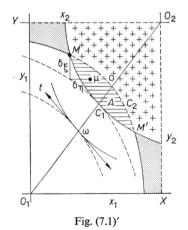

Fig. (7.1)′

by diminishing that of I_2; while in the white region one can augment the satisfaction of I_2 but only at the expense of the satisfaction of I_1.

In conclusion one sees that every point μ of A is preferable to M and can be achieved by an exchange in which I_1 hands over a certain quantity of η, and I_2 a certain quantity of ξ. Thus M is not Pareto-optimal. It is equally clear that if I_1 and I_2 are individuals then – without introducing other hypotheses – we cannot assert that the two individuals will come to an understanding about the realization of such exchanges, or know the definite result of such a change. It would be nearly the same if, modifying our example slightly, we imagine that I_1 and I_2 are the production processes of two different goods, utilizing the same factors ξ and η for producing the goods whose quantity is measured this time by $f_1(x_1, y_1)$ and $f_2(x_2, y_2)$, and between which a center of decision would have to choose. It is, however, sufficient to introduce the market-conditions of the two goods to determine the allocation of factors between the two production processes.

In any case one can say that objectively the exchange must be stopped if one starts from a point ω of O_1O_2, or if, after starting from M, one arrives at a point of the segment $O'O''$ where O_1O_2 intersects the region A. In fact, at the points O_1O_2 the curves C_1 and C_2 not only have common tangents, but are also situated on different sides of their common tangent, which excludes the possibility of mutual improvements for I_1 and I_2.

EXAMPLE (7.2).

We will now treat algebraically an analogous example which is, however, a little more general in the sense that we shall consider N individuals among whom we have for allocation the quantity X of ξ, and the quantity Y of η. The preference-functions f_j for each individual I_j are of the same type as before, namely: $f_j(x_j, y_j) = x_j y_j$.

This time we shall try to find directly the sets of Pareto-optimal distributions described by the points P:

$$
\begin{array}{lll}
I_1 & x_1, & y_1 \\
I_2 & x_2, & y_2 \\
\vdots & & \\
I_j & x_j, & y_j \\
\vdots & & \\
I_N & x_N, & y_N
\end{array}
$$

where

$$ x_j \geqslant 0, y_j \geqslant 0 \qquad \sum_j x_j = X \qquad \sum_j y_j = Y $$

having the property that no exchange can be made starting from P without damaging the situation of at least one individual.

Having given exactly the condition of Pareto optimality which we impose, we can confine ourselves at the beginning to exchanges between two arbitrary individuals only. We shall obtain relatively weak necessary conditions which we shall extend, as it were, in all directions until we obtain conditions which we shall prove to be sufficient (according to the brief account of Chapter I).

Let now $x_1{}^0$, $y_1{}^0$ and $x_2{}^0$, $y_2{}^0$ be the assignments of I_1 and I_2 at the start. Let us search for conditions which will exclude the existence of algebraic exchanges, δx and δy for I_1, and $-\delta x$, $-\delta y$ for I_2. augmenting at least one of the satisfactions of I_1 and I_2, and not diminishing the other.

Thus it must be inadmissible to have simultaneously

either   or

$$f_1(x_1{}^0 + \delta x, y_1{}^0 + \delta y) > f_1(x_1{}^0, y_1{}^0) \,\bigg|\, f_1(x_1{}^0 + \delta x, y_1{}^0 + \delta y) > f_1(x_1{}^0, y_1{}^0)$$
$$f_2(x_2{}^0 - \delta x, y_2{}^0 - \delta y) > f_2(x_2{}^0, y_2{}^0) \,\bigg|\, f_2(x_2{}^0 - \delta x, y_2{}^0 - \delta y) = f_1(x_2{}^0, y_2{}^0)$$

or

$$f_1(x_1{}^0 + \delta x, y_1{}^0 + \delta y) = f_1(x_1{}^0, y_1{}^0)$$
$$f_2(x_2{}^0 - \delta x, y_2{}^0 - \delta y) > f_2(x_2{}^0, y_2{}^0)$$

i.e. in brief

$$f_1(x_1{}^0 + \delta x, y_1{}^0 + \delta y) \geqslant f_1(x_1{}^0, y_1{}^0)$$

and

$$f_2(x_2{}^0 - \delta x, y_2{}^0 - \delta y) \geqslant f_2(x_2{}^0, y_2{}^0).$$

with at least one strict inequality.

Let us investigate analytically under what conditions for example can one have

$$f_1(x_1{}^0 + \delta x, y_1{}^0 + \delta y) \geqslant f(x_1{}^0, y_1{}^0)$$

Suppressing, except at the end, all indices, this gives

$$(x + \delta x)(y + \delta y) \geqslant xy$$
$$y\delta x + x\delta y + \delta x\delta y \geqslant 0$$
$$\delta x(y + \delta y) + x\delta y \geqslant 0$$
$$\delta x(y + \delta y) \geqslant -x\,\delta y$$

and since $y + \delta y$ must remain positive

$$\delta x \geqslant -\frac{x}{y + \delta y}\,\delta y$$

or

$$\delta x \geqslant -\frac{x_1{}^0}{y_1{}^0 + \delta y}\,\delta y.$$

But the same condition applies to f_2 also if δx and δy are replaced by $-\delta x$ and $-\delta y$, hence

$$-\delta x \geqslant -\frac{x_2{}^0}{y_2{}^0 - \delta y}\,(-\delta y)$$

or

$$\delta x \leqslant -\frac{x_2{}^0}{y_2{}^0 - \delta y}\,\delta y$$

The set of these conditions can be summed up by

$$\frac{-x_1{}^0}{y_1{}^0 + \delta y}\,\delta y \leqslant \delta x \leqslant -\frac{x_2{}^0}{y_2{}^0 - \delta y}\,\delta y.$$

We must fix δy a priori so small in absolute value, that the new assignments of I_1 and I_2 should still be positive or zero.

Indeed, what we want to assure, is that it will be impossible to find a δx and a δy satisfying these conditions simultaneously with at least one strict inequality sign in the above statement, i.e. we want to *exclude* the possibility that we have

$$-\frac{x_1^0}{y_1^0 + \delta y}\delta y < -\frac{x_2^0}{y_2^0 - \delta y}\delta y$$

Or, to put it in the other way round, we *must* have

$$-\frac{x_2^0}{y_2^0 - \delta y}\delta y \leqslant -\frac{x_1^0}{y_1^0 + \delta y}\delta y$$

for any y such that both expressions $(y_0^2 - \delta y)$ and $(y_1^0 + \delta y)$ are strictly positive.

This is necessary to have a Pareto-optimal allocation in the above example.

Two cases can thus arise: (1) $\delta y > 0$; (2) $\delta y < 0$.
If $\delta y > 0$, one must have

$$\frac{-x_2^0}{y_2^0 - \delta y} \leqslant \frac{-x_1^0}{y_1^0 + \delta y}$$

or

$$\frac{y_2^0 - \delta y}{x_2^0} \leqslant \frac{y_1^0 + \delta y}{x_1^0}$$

which can be written as

$$\left(\frac{y_2^0}{x_2^0} - \frac{y_1^0}{x_1^0}\right) \leqslant \delta y\left(\frac{1}{x_2^0} + \frac{1}{x_1^0}\right).$$

If $\delta y < 0$, one must reverse the sign of the inequalities, which gives

$$\left(\frac{y_2^0}{x_2^0} - \frac{y_1^0}{x_1^0}\right) \geqslant \delta y\left(\frac{1}{x_2^0} + \frac{1}{x_1^0}\right).$$

These conditions must be satisfied whatever the absolute value of δy making the assignments of I_1 and I_2 positive. Thus, it is evident that they can be fulfilled only if $(y_2^0/x_2^0 - y_1^0/x_1^0) \equiv 0$, and that in this case they are fulfilled for every value of the variation δy, which is admissible for the nature of the problem.

Thus we have finally arrived at the necessary condition (omitting the index 0)

$$\frac{y_1}{x_1} = \frac{y_2}{x_2}.$$

But it is abundantly clear that we can establish in the same way that the first ratio y_1/x_1 must be equal to any corresponding ratio y_i/x_i, which gives a set of necessary conditions.

$$\frac{y_1}{x_1} = \frac{y_2}{x_2} = \cdots = \frac{y_j}{x_j} = \cdots = \frac{y_N}{x_N} = \text{consequently } \frac{Y}{X}.$$

Thus one can give the x_j arbitrarily subject to the only condition that their sum is X. Then one determines the y by

$$\begin{cases} y_1 = x_1 \dfrac{Y}{X} \\ \vdots \\ y_j = x_j \dfrac{Y}{X} \\ \vdots \\ y_N = x_N \dfrac{Y}{X} \end{cases}$$

Thus the region of optimality Ω reduces in the $2N$-dimensional space $x_1, y_1, \ldots, x_N, y_N$ at most to a *positive* region Ω' of only $N - 1$ dimensions (since, for example, only $N - 1$ x can be given arbitrarily).

It finally remains to identify Ω exactly. It is very easy to see that Ω is identical to Ω'. In fact, let us put $Y/X = \lambda$.

The coordinates of a point ρ' of Ω' are

$$x_1, \lambda x_1; \quad x_j, \lambda x_j; \quad x_N, \lambda x_N$$

where

$$\Sigma x_j = X$$

We will prove that for any other point M with coordinates $\overline{x_j}, \overline{y_j}$, it is impossible that one should have for every j:

(1) $$f_j(\overline{x_j}, \overline{y_j}) \geqslant f_j(x_j, \lambda x_j)$$

In fact, one can put

$$\overline{x_j} = x_j + \delta x_j$$
$$\overline{y_j} = \lambda x_j + \lambda \delta y_j$$

with the conditions

$$\sum_j \delta x_j = \sum_j \lambda \delta y_j = \sum_j \delta y_j = 0.$$

The inequality (1) requires that

$$\lambda(x_j + \delta x_j)(x_j + \delta y_j) \geqslant \lambda x_j^2$$

or

$$(x_j + \delta x_j)(x_j + \delta y_j) \geqslant x_j^2$$

However, among the couples of positive numbers which have the same product, the minimum sum is attained for two equal numbers. (The reader will find the proof of this extremal result in the example (12.1′).

Thus

$$x_j + \delta x_j + x_j + \delta y_j \geqslant x_j + x_j$$

or

$$\delta x_j + \delta y_j \geqslant 0.$$

Since this inequality is sharp for at least one value of j, summing these inequalities one clearly obtains

$$\sum_j \delta x_j + \sum_j \delta y_j > 0$$

which contradicts the binding condition

$$\Sigma \, \delta x_j = \Sigma \, \delta y_j = 0.$$

Thus the hypothesis implying this contradiction must be rejected. The set Ω'

$$y_j = \lambda x_j \qquad \Sigma \, x_j = X$$

is thus truly the Pareto-optimal set Ω we were looking for.

REMARKS

1. To establish in example (7.2) that $y_1/x_1 = y_2/x_2$, we could have applied the results of example (7.1). We have not done this in order to give an example of the algebraic method which is more general and can be utilized more systematically than the geometric method.

2. In example (7.2) we have been able to prove completely rigorously that Ω is a global optimum. This is rather exceptional, since while generally speaking it is relatively easy to find necessary conditions of optimality, in general, one can only find sufficient conditions of a local nature.

3. Finally, in (7.2), the reader could prove that starting from a point $P(x_j, y_j)$ not in Ω, the point

$$Q \left(\frac{\lambda \, x_j + y_j}{2}, \frac{\lambda \, x_j + y_j}{2} \right)$$

of Ω is superior to P for each individual.

Intuitive explanation of the Pareto optimality

Let us attempt to give an intuitive explanation of the peculiarity pointed out in the last paragraph of page (50) and illustrated by the figure (7.7).

Let us assume, as above, that c and C are constraints, weak and strong respectively, and let us confine ourselves – when discussing the optimality or non-optimality – to points which satisfy C. Thus, for every point situated inside curve C, the question is whether it is an optimum under the constraints c and C respectively. When we examine whether or not a point (satisfying C) is an optimum under c, we shall also have to take into consideration, as terms of comparison, points which do not satisfy C, but satisfy c. The fact that (among the points which satisfy C) the class of points optimal under C is not less numerous than the class of points

58

optimal under c, can be explained intuitively by this consideration: to require that a point (satisfying C) – for example, the point A – should be an optimum under C is not more exacting than to require that it should be an optimum under c. In fact, C represents a stronger requirement than c regarding the points which serve as comparison for A when optimality or non-optimality of A is discussed. Thus, the number of points to be compared with A is less when we examine if A is an optimum under C than under c.

LINEAR EQUATIONS

In order to support certain lines of argument to which we shall turn in other chapters, we shall present here the theory of linear equations. In order to be as simple and clear as possible, we shall proceed in the following way: first, we shall discuss in detail the case when only a rather small number of unknowns are present (making the understanding easy) and will give rigorous proofs for our conclusions. Then, we will be able to deduce from this the general theory by analogy. While we will refrain from giving rigorous proofs in the general case, we shall state the relevant theorems in a precise and complete form.

In the discussion we will make use of determinants. The essential elements of the theory of determinants can be found in Chapter XIII.

One linear equation with one variable

Let us begin by considering the possibilities which can arise in the case of one equation with one unknown.

$$(8.1) \qquad\qquad ax = b$$

where a and b are *given* constants and x is the unknown to be determined. Here one must distinguish four possibilities according to whether $a \neq 0$ or $a = 0$, and whether $b \neq 0$ or $b = 0$. The first case: $a \neq 0$ has two "sub-cases": when $b \neq 0$, and when $b = 0$, this distinction, however, is of very little significance.

If we bring these two secondary possibilities under the principal case, we have the following three cases:

(I) $a \neq 0$ and b is arbitrary
(II) $a = 0$ and $b \neq 0$
(III) $a = 0$ and $b = 0$.

In the case (I) the equation (8.1) has *one and only one solution*, namely

$x = b/a$ (whether the solution is equal to zero as when $b = 0$, or is different from zero as when $b \neq 0$ is of little interest in the present context; what is important is that there is one and only one solution). In case (II), the equation (8.1) has no (finite) solution. In case (III), the equation (8.1) has an infinity of solutions: every finite number is a solution.

We are going to find again the principle of these three types (I), (II) and (III) when we deal with linear equations in several unknowns.

Two linear equations with two variables

Let us consider at first a system of two equations in two unknowns.

(8.2)
$$a_{11}x_1 + a_{12}x_2 = b_1$$
$$a_{21}x_1 + a_{22}x_2 = b_2.$$

If we multiply the first equation by a_{22} and the second equation by a_{12}, and take the difference, we obtain

(8.3)
$$\begin{vmatrix} a_{11} & a_{12} \\ a_{21} & a_{22} \end{vmatrix} x_1 = \begin{vmatrix} b_1 & a_{12} \\ b_2 & a_{22} \end{vmatrix}$$

And if we multiply the first equation by a_{21} and the second by a_{11}, and take the difference, we obtain

(8.4)
$$\begin{vmatrix} a_{11} & a_{12} \\ a_{21} & a_{22} \end{vmatrix} x_2 = \begin{vmatrix} a_{11} & b_1 \\ a_{21} & b_2 \end{vmatrix}$$

Equations (8.3) and (8.4) can now each be discussed in the same way as the equation in one unknown above. Considering (8.3) and (8.4) alike, the case when there exists a *unique solution* is characterised as the case when the second-order determinant formed from the coefficients on the left-hand side of (8.2) is not zero.

When this determinant is equal to zero, that is

(8.5)
$$\begin{vmatrix} a_{11} & a_{12} \\ a_{21} & a_{22} \end{vmatrix} = 0,$$

it will be *necessary* for the existence of a finite solution $(x_1 x_2)$ that we should have simultaneously

(8.6)
$$\begin{vmatrix} b_1 & a_{12} \\ b_2 & a_{22} \end{vmatrix} = 0 \quad \text{and} \quad \begin{vmatrix} a_{11} & b_1 \\ a_{21} & b_2 \end{vmatrix} = 0.$$

If (8.5) is satisfied, but (8.6) is not, there is no solution $(x_1 x_2)$. If both (8.5) and (8.6) are satisfied, there *may* be a solution.

Whether or not there exists a solution depends on the properties of the coefficients. If among the coefficients of the second-order matrix of the left-hand side at least one is not zero, there always exists a solution $(x_1 x_2)$. Let us assume, for example, that $a_{22} \neq 0$. We can now write

$$(8.7) \qquad x_2 = \frac{b_2 - a_{21}x_1}{a_{22}}.$$

Substituting this value of x_2 into the left-hand side of (8.2), we obtain

$$(8.8) \qquad a_{11}x_1 + \frac{a_{12}}{a_{22}}(b_2 - a_{21}x_1) = \frac{a_{12}b_2}{a_{22}} + \frac{\begin{vmatrix} a_{11} & a_{12} \\ a_{21} & a_{22} \end{vmatrix}}{a_{22}} x_1.$$

The second term on the right-hand side vanishes in virtue of (8.5) and the first one will be equal to b_1 in virtue of the first equation of (8.6). In other words, if (8.5) and (8.6) are both satisfied, and if $a_{22} \neq 0$, we can satisfy both equations (8.2) by giving x_1 an arbitrary value (positive, negative, or zero) and then determining x_2 with the help of (8.7).

We arrive at an analogous conclusion if a_{22} is zero but one of the three other coefficients of the left-hand side of (8.2) is not zero. In each case, *one* of the unknowns can be chosen arbitrarily, but the second will necessarily be a determined linear function of the first one.

Let us suppose now that the four coefficients of the left-hand side of (8.2) are all zero. In this case, it is not certain that the system has a (finite) solution. That depends on the values of the coefficients b_1 and b_2 on the right-hand side. For the existence of a solution in this case it is necessary that $b_1 = 0$ and that $b_2 = 0$. Moreover, if this condition is fulfilled any pair of (finite) numbers $(x_1 x_2)$ will do.

Thus in this case the solution has *two* degrees of freedom, while in the case when one of the four coefficients of the left-hand side of (8.2) is not zero, it has only one. Moreover, when (8.5) is not satisfied, that is when the determinant of the coefficients on the left-hand side is not zero, there exists one solution, and this solution has no degree of freedom.

Three linear equations with three variables

Let us consider next a system of three equations in three unknowns.

$$
\begin{aligned}
a_{11}x_1 + a_{12}x_2 + a_{13}x_3 &= b_1 \\
a_{21}x_1 + a_{22}x_2 + a_{23}x_3 &= b_2 \\
a_{31}x_1 + a_{32}x_2 + a_{33}x_3 &= b_3 .
\end{aligned}
$$

(8.9)

By the method of elimination, analogous to the one above, we obtain

(8.10)

$$
\begin{vmatrix} a_{11}a_{12}a_{13} \\ a_{21}a_{22}a_{23} \\ a_{31}a_{32}a_{33} \end{vmatrix} x_1 = \begin{vmatrix} b_1 a_{12}a_{13} \\ b_2 a_{22}a_{23} \\ b_3 a_{32}a_{33} \end{vmatrix}
$$

$$
\begin{vmatrix} a_{11}a_{12}a_{13} \\ a_{21}a_{22}a_{23} \\ a_{31}a_{32}a_{33} \end{vmatrix} x_2 = \begin{vmatrix} a_{11}b_1 a_{13} \\ a_{21}b_2 a_{23} \\ a_{31}b_3 a_{33} \end{vmatrix}
$$

$$
\begin{vmatrix} a_{11}a_{12}a_{13} \\ a_{21}a_{22}a_{12} \\ a_{31}a_{32}a_{33} \end{vmatrix} x_3 = \begin{vmatrix} a_{11}a_{12}b_1 \\ a_{21}a_{22}b_2 \\ a_{31}a_{32}b_3 \end{vmatrix}
$$

We see that, for the existence of a *unique* solution $(x_1 x_2 x_3)$, it is necessary that the determinant of the coefficients on the left-hand side of (8.9) should not be zero. If it is not zero we can divide the three equations (8.10) by it and find the only values of $(x_1 x_2 x_3)$ which can be solutions of the system of equations (8.9). Moreover, we can verify by substitution that these values $(x_1 x_2 x_3)$ will in fact satisfy all three equations. Thus, a *necessary and sufficient* condition for $(x_1 x_2 x_3)$ to be a solution of the system of equations is that it should consist of the above calculated values.

On the other hand, if the third-order determinant of the coefficients on the left-hand side is zero, that is

(8.11)
$$
\begin{vmatrix} a_{11}a_{12}a_{13} \\ a_{21}a_{22}a_{23} \\ a_{31}a_{32}a_{33} \end{vmatrix} = 0 ,
$$

it is no longer certain that there is a solution. In fact, to have a solution it is *necessary* that in addition, the condition

(8.12)
$$
\begin{vmatrix} b_1 a_{12}a_{13} \\ b_2 a_{22}a_{23} \\ b_3 a_{32}a_{33} \end{vmatrix} = 0 \quad \begin{vmatrix} a_{11}b_1 a_{13} \\ a_{21}b_2 a_{23} \\ a_{31}b_3 a_{33} \end{vmatrix} = 0 \quad \begin{vmatrix} a_{11}a_{12}b_1 \\ a_{21}a_{22}b_2 \\ a_{31}a_{32}b_3 \end{vmatrix} = 0 .
$$

should also be satisfied. Whether or not there exists a solution in the case (8.11)–(8.12) depends on the structure of the coefficients. If, in the coefficient-matrix of the left-hand side of (8.9), we find at least one non-zero second-order determinant, the situation is clear. Suppose, for example, that the determinant situated in the lower right-hand corner is not zero, i.e.

$$\begin{vmatrix} a_{22} a_{23} \\ a_{32} a_{33} \end{vmatrix} \neq 0.$$

In this case, as is shown by the discussion of the equation in two unknowns, we can always determine x_2 and x_3. The expressions obtained will now depend on x_1 (at least when a_{21} and a_{31} are not both zero, but whether this special case arises or not has no influence on the following line of argument). Substituting these expressions for x_2 and x_3 into the equations of (8.9), and assuming that (8.11) and (8.12) are satisfied, we note that all three equations will be satisfied whatever the value (positive, negative, or zero) of x_1. Thus in this case there exists a solution, and this solution has *one* degree of freedom. We obtain the same result if

$$\begin{vmatrix} a_{22} a_{23} \\ a_{32} a_{33} \end{vmatrix} = 0$$

but (at least) one of the other second-order determinants is different from zero. The two unknowns which correspond to the non-zero second order determinant can always be expressed as functions of the third one.

When *all* the second-order determinants contained in the third-order matrix of the coefficients on the left-hand side are zero, we find ourselves in a new situation. There will exist no (finite) solutions, unless other *necessary* conditions are also fulfilled. To define these conditions, we consider, for example, the first two equations and assume that they are written as equations in x_2 and x_3. The right-hand sides of these equations will be $(b_1 - a_{11}x_1)$ and $(b_2 - a_{21}x_1)$. The determinant of the coefficients on the left-hand side is

$$\begin{vmatrix} a_{12} a_{13} \\ a_{22} a_{23} \end{vmatrix}$$

and is zero by hypothesis. The discussion relating to equations with two unknowns shows that it is necessary to have

(8.13) $\quad \begin{vmatrix} (b_1 - a_{11}x_1) a_{13} \\ (b_2 - a_{21}x_1) a_{23} \end{vmatrix} = 0 \quad \begin{vmatrix} a_{12} (b_1 - a_{11}x_1) \\ a_{22} (b_2 - a_{21}x_1) \end{vmatrix} = 0.$

64

The first condition, arranged in terms of x_1, gives

$$\begin{vmatrix} b_1 a_{13} \\ b_2 a_{23} \end{vmatrix} - \begin{vmatrix} a_{11} a_{13} \\ a_{21} a_{23} \end{vmatrix} x_1 = 0.$$

Thus we have:

$$\begin{vmatrix} b_1 a_{13} \\ b_2 a_{23} \end{vmatrix} = 0.$$

Similarly, we must have:

$$\begin{vmatrix} a_{12} b_1 \\ a_{22} b_2 \end{vmatrix} = 0.$$

In other words, the conditions to be fulfilled are completely analogous to those which we had defined in the case of two equations in two unknowns, when the second-order determinant of the coefficients on the left hand side was zero. To sum up, we find that in the case when all the second-order determinants contained in the third-order determinant of the coefficients on the left-hand side of (8.9) are zero, there exists no solution unless the following *necessary* condition is also fulfilled:

CONDITION (8.14). All second-order determinants which can be formed by choosing from two lines of (8.9) a column of the right-hand coefficients, and a column of the left-hand coefficients, are necessarily zero. Thus, for example,

$$\begin{vmatrix} b_1 a_{12} \\ b_2 a_{22} \end{vmatrix} = 0, \quad \begin{vmatrix} a_{11} b_1 \\ a_{21} b_2 \end{vmatrix} = 0, \quad \text{etc...}$$

If it satisfies the condition (8.14), the system *may* have a solution. If at least one of the coefficients of the left-hand side is non-zero, the situation is clear. Let us assume, for example, that $a_{13} \neq 0$. We can, from the first equation, express x_3 as a function of x_1 and x_2. Substituting this expression into the second and third equations, we find that the three equations will be satisfied whatever the values we give to x_1 and x_2, provided that all the second-order determinants contained in the matrix of coefficients on the left-hand side of (8.9) are zero, and that (8.14) is satisfied. In other words, the solution now has *two* degrees of freedom. It will be the same if $a_{13} = 0$, but one (at least) of the coefficients on the left-hand side is non-zero. If *all* the coefficients on the left-hand side are zero, the solution requires a new necessary condition: all the b must be zero. If this condition is not fulfilled, there is no solution. If it is fulfilled, there exists a solution having *three* degrees of freedom: it is possible to give arbitrary (finite) values to the unknowns x_1, x_2, x_3.

A system of n equations in n unknowns

Having reviewed in this way the case of one, two and three unknowns, we can discuss the case of a system of n linear equations with n unknowns that is a system of the form

(8.15)
$$
\begin{aligned}
a_{11}x_1 + a_{12}x_2 + \cdots + a_{1n}x_n &= b_1 \\
a_{21}x_1 + a_{22}x_2 + \cdots + a_{2n}x_n &= b_2 \\
&\cdots\cdots\cdots\cdots\cdots\cdots\cdots \\
a_{n1}x_1 + a_{n2}x_2 + \cdots + a_{nn}x_n &= b_n
\end{aligned}
$$

or, in a more condensed form:

(8.16)
$$\sum_k a_{hk}x_k = b_h \qquad (h = 1, 2, \ldots n),$$

where the summation $\sum_k$ stands for $\sum_{k=1}^{n}$.

We shall consider at first formulae which represent unconditionally valid identities, independent of the structure of the coefficient-matrix (a_{ij}). Later we shall study separately the case when the matrix (a_{ij}) is of rank n, and the case when it is of rank $(n-1)$.

The elements of the adjoint

Let $\hat{a}_{ih}$ be the elements of the adjoint of the matrix (a_{ij}) (cp. Chapter XIII). The adjoint elements exist whatever the structure of the matrix (a_{ij}). These are going to furnish us with especially useful information concerning important data of the problem. Let us multiply (8.16) by $\hat{a}_{ih}$ and sum with respect to h. The result is

(8.17)
$$\sum_h \sum_k \hat{a}_{ih} a_{hk} x_k = \sum_h \hat{a}_{ih} b_h.$$

On the left-hand side, the summation with respect to h gives (in virtue of (13.25) $\sum_h \hat{a}_{ih} a_{hk} = |a| \cdot e_{ik}$, where $|a|$ is the value of the determinant of the coefficient matrix (a_{ij}) of the left-hand side of (8.15), and where

$$
e_{ik} = \begin{cases} 1, & \text{if } i = k \\ 0, & \text{if } i \neq k. \end{cases}
$$

66

The equality (8.17) can thus be written as

$$|a| \cdot \sum_k e_{ik}x_k = \sum_h \hat{a}_{ih}b_h,$$

that is

(8.18) $\quad |a| \cdot x_i = \sum_h \hat{a}_{ih}b_h = \begin{vmatrix} a_{11}a_{12} \dots \{b_1\} \dots a_{1n} \\ a_{21}a_{22} \dots \{b_2\} \dots a_{2n} \\ \dots\dots\dots\dots\dots \\ a_{n1}\,a_{n2}\,\dots\,\{b_n\}\,\dots\,a_{nn} \end{vmatrix} \quad (i = 1, 2, \dots n).$

The curly brackets on the right-hand side of (8.18) indicate that we have substituted $b_1, \dots, b_n$ for the elements $a_{1i}, \dots a_{ni}$ in the i-th column of the matrix (a).

We can now say that if there exists a solution $(x_1 \dots x_n)$ of (8.15), it must satisfy (8.18), that is, this solution is necessarily a homogeneous *linear form* of the coefficients $(b_1 \dots b_n)$ of the right-hand side.

Cramer's formula and its application in the non-singular case

Let us consider at first the case when the matrix (a) is of rank n, i.e. when the determinant $|a|$ is not zero. It follows from (8.18) that if there exists a system of solutions $(x_1 \dots x_n)$, this system must be determined uniquely. In fact, we can divide (8.18) by $|a|$, which gives us

(8.19) $\quad x_i = \dfrac{1}{|a|} \cdot \sum_h \hat{a}_{ih}b_h = \dfrac{\begin{vmatrix} a_{11}a_{12} \dots \{b_1\} \dots a_{1n} \\ a_{21}a_{22} \dots \{b_2\} \dots a_{2n} \\ \dots\dots\dots\dots\dots \\ a_{n1}\,a_{n2}\,\dots\,\{b_n\}\,\dots\,a_{nn} \end{vmatrix}}{\begin{vmatrix} a_{11}a_{12} \dots\dots\dots a_{1n} \\ a_{21}a_{22} \dots\dots\dots a_{2n} \\ \dots\dots\dots\dots\dots \\ a_{n1}\,a_{n2}\,\dots\dots\dots\,a_{nn} \end{vmatrix}} \quad (i = 1, 2, \dots n).$

That is *Cramer's formula*, which is used to solve a system of linear equations. It applies in the case, and only in the case, when $|a| \neq 0$.

The above argument proves only that if there exists a solution system $(x_1 \dots x_n)$ and if $|a|$ is not zero, this system is necessarily uniquely determined, and satisfies (8.19). But it is easy to see that if $|a| \neq 0$, the solution given by (8.19) does in fact satisfy the system of equations (8.16), as can be seen by substituting (8.19) into the left-hand side of (8.16). It gives

$$\frac{1}{|a|} \sum_k a_{hk} \sum_s \hat{a}_{ks} b_s .$$

Since

$$\sum_k a_{hk} \hat{a}_{ks} = |a| \cdot e_{hs} ,$$

this expression reduces to $\sum_s e_{hs} b_s = b_h$, which is identical to the right-hand side of (8.16).

Thus when $|a| \neq 0$, there exists one solution system, and one only, namely (8.19).

Sometimes it is useful to express the result as a single formula. This can be obtained by forming a linear combination of the solutions $x_1 \ldots x_n$ of (8.15) with arbitrary coefficients $\theta_1 \ldots \theta_n$. In view of (8.19), this combination can be written in the form

$$\theta_1 x_1 + \theta_2 x_2 + \cdots + \theta_n x_n = \frac{1}{|a|} \sum_h \sum_k \theta_h \hat{a}_{hk} b_k$$

(8.20)

$$= - \frac{\begin{vmatrix} 0 & \theta_1 & \theta_2 & \ldots \theta_n \\ b_1 a_{11} a_{12} \ldots a_{1n} \\ b_2 a_{21} a_{22} \ldots a_{2n} \\ \ldots\ldots\ldots\ldots\ldots \\ b_n a_{n1} a_{n2} \ldots a_{nn} \end{vmatrix}}{\begin{vmatrix} a_{11} a_{12} \ldots a_{1n} \\ a_{21} a_{22} \ldots a_{2n} \\ \ldots\ldots\ldots\ldots \\ a_{n1} a_{n2} \ldots a_{nn} \end{vmatrix}}$$

If in (8.20) we make every θ equal to zero except θ_i, which we take to be 1, we obtain (8.19) again.

There exist various very effective methods of calculating numerically the right-hand side of (8.19) even when the number of unknowns is very considerable, and may, perhaps, be counted in hundreds. Both methods of approximation and exact methods are available.

Theorems concerning homogeneous systems which have the same number of equations as unknowns

Let us raise now a new question: We consider the uniquely determined solution system, which exists when $|a| \neq 0$. Are all the $x_1 \ldots x_n$ equal to zero, or is there *at least one x* which is *different from zero?* This is a very important question in numerous practical cases.

We see that if $b_1 \ldots b_n$ are all zero, then all the $x_1 \ldots x_n$ must also be zero, by reason of (8.19). Thus, by defining a *homogeneous* system of equations as a system of the form (8.15) where all the $b_1 \ldots b_n$ are zero, we can state the following theorem.

THEOREM (8.21). A homogeneous system of linear equations, which has the same number of equations as unknowns, and whose coefficient-determinant $|a|$ is not zero, can have no other solution than $x_1 = x_2 = \ldots = x_n = 0$.

The following theorem expresses the same fact in another form.

THEOREM (8.22). A homogeneous system of linear equations having the same number of equations as unknowns cannot have a solution in which not all the unknowns are zero unless the coefficient-determinant of the system is zero.

In particular, we shall need this theorem to establish (10.16).

Now let us consider the case when the coefficient matrix (a) of (8.16) is of rank $(n-1)$; that is the case when $|a| = 0$, but at least one of the sub-determinants of order $(n-1)$ of (a) is not zero. First we examine the conditions required for the existence of solutions, then those which must be fulfilled in order that there should exist a solution system where not all the $x_1 \ldots x_n$ are zero. It will be confirmed that if $|a| = 0$ (which is necessarily the case when (a) is of rank $(n-1)$, one can find a solution system where not all the $x_1 \ldots x_n$ are zero.

(8.18) at once stipulates a necessary condition for the existence of solutions in the case when $|a| = 0$. Whatever are the (finite) values of $x_1 \ldots x_n$, the left hand side must be zero in this case. In other words, we must have

(8.23) $$\sum_h \hat{a}_{ih} b_h = 0 \quad \text{for} \quad i = 1, 2, \ldots n.$$

This can also be written as

$$(8.24) \qquad \begin{vmatrix} a_{11}a_{12} \dots \overset{i}{\{b_1\}} \dots a_{1n} \\ a_{21}a_{22} \dots \{b_2\} \dots a_{2n} \\ \dots\dots\dots\dots\dots \\ a_{n1}\,a_{n2} \dots \{b_n\} \dots a_{nn} \end{vmatrix} = 0 \quad \text{for} \quad i = 1, 2, \dots n.$$

This expression generalises the conditions which resulted from the discussion of the cases $n = 1, 2, 3$.

Thus, if $|a| = 0$, (8.24) represents a necessary condition for the existence of a solution system $(x_1 \dots x_n)$. When (a) is of rank $(n-1)$ – which means that not only is $|a| = 0$ but at least one of the sub-determinants of order $(n-1)$ of (a) is not zero – (8.24) represents not only a necessary but at the same time also a *sufficient* condition for the existence of a solution system.

To say that one can find a sub-determinant of order $(n-1)$ of (a) different from zero is the same as to say that at least one element in the adjoint $(\hat{a})$ is not zero. Let us assume that $\hat{a}_{RS}$ is this element. We have thus

$$(8.25) \qquad\qquad\qquad \hat{a}_{RS} \neq 0,$$

where R and S are now two fixed indices, i.e.

$$(8.26) \qquad \begin{vmatrix} a_{11}a_{12} \dots) a_{1R} (\dots a_{1n} \\ a_{21}a_{22} \dots) a_{2R} (\dots a_{2n} \\ \dots\dots\dots\dots\dots \\ ) a_{S1}a_{S2} \dots\dots\dots a_{Sn} (\\ \dots\dots\dots\dots\dots \\ a_{n1}\,a_{n2} \dots) a_{nR} (\dots a_{nn} \end{vmatrix} \neq 0.$$

The determinant (8.26) is the one obtained from $|a|$ by suppressing the S-th row and the R-th column.

Let us return now to the system of equations (8.15).

We omit the S-th equation, and carry the terms in x_R over to the right-hand side. We obtain in this way a system of $(n-1)$ linear equations in $(n-1)$ unknowns $x_1 \dots) x_R (\dots x_n$. Because of (8.26), the coefficient-determinant of this system is not zero. Thus the system can be uniquely solved with respect to the $(n-1)$ unknowns $x_1 \dots) x_R (\dots x_n$. This result is obtained by applying (8.19) to the $(n-1)$ dimensional system under consideration. It is easy to see that each x_r of $x_1 \dots) x_R (\dots x_n$ becomes in this way a linear form of x_R, that is, a constant term (depending on r) plus

70

another constant (depending on r) multiplied by x_R. Thus, the solution system will contain x_R as an arbitrary parameter.

Substituting this solution system into the initial equations, one finds in virtue of (8.24) that the n equations (8.15) are all satisfied whatever the value assigned to x_R.

Not only does there exist a solution system which can be constructed in this way, but moreover, if this construction incorporates an arbitrary parameter, this system generates all the solutions of the system of equations.

Since there exists a solution system in which one of the unknowns can be chosen arbitrarily, one can always find – provided that the matrix (a) is of rank $(n-1)$ and satisfies (8.24) – a solution system $(x_1 \ldots x_n)$ in which the $x_1 \ldots x_n$ will *not all* be simultaneously zero.

In the special case of a *homogeneous* system, the conditions (8.24) will always be fulfilled, whatever the coefficients a_{ij}. Hence the following theorem:

THEOREM (8.27). A homogeneous system of linear equations which has the same number of equations as unknowns and whose determinant $|a|$ is of rank $(n-1)$ always has solutions, and among these solutions there is a solution system where the $x_1 \ldots x_n$ are not all simultaneously zero. (cf. the generalisation stated in (8.31).)

In the above case, the solutions can be expressed in a particularly simple form. When (8.25) is satisfied, one can put

$$(8.28) \qquad x_r = \frac{\hat{a}_{rS}}{\hat{a}_{RS}} x_R$$

($r=1, 2, \ldots, n$, in the case of a homogeneous system of rank $(n-1)$.)

This means that one can simply define the unknowns $x_1 \ldots x_n$ as proportional to the elements of a column of the adjoint in which column there is at least one non-zero element. It matters little which column we choose (provided it contains a non-zero element) because all the columns of the adjoint of a singular (square) matrix (i.e. a matrix whose determinant is zero) are proportional. The factor of proportionality between $x_1 \ldots x_n$ and the elements of the chosen column are *arbitrary*. That is only another way of saying that the solution now has one degree of freedom. Thus, we can express (8.28) in the form

$$(8.29) \qquad x_r = v\hat{a}_{rS}$$

($r = 1, 2, \ldots, n$, in the case of a homogeneous system of rank $(n-1)$.), S being a column of $(\hat{a})$ containing at least one non-zero element, and v is an arbitrary parameter.

By substituting (8.28) into the left-hand side of (8.15), we can now verify that (8.28) satisfies all the equations (8.15) when the system is homogeneous (i.e. when all the $b_1 \ldots b_n = 0$). It gives

$$\sum_k a_{hk} \frac{\hat{a}_{kS}}{\hat{a}_{RS}} x_R = |a| \cdot e_{hS} x_R,$$

which is zero if $|a|$ is zero.

The facts expressed by the formulae (8.28) – (8.29) can be put to good use when, for example, we wish to find the extremum of a quadratic form using the method expounded in (10.14)–(10–16), or in the case of the general problem studied in Chapter XI.

If the system (a) is of rank equal to or less than $(n-2)$, then for the existence of solutions of the system (8.15) it is *necessary* that all the determinants of order $(n-1)$ which can be formed by taking (8.24) and eliminating in every possible way one row and one column (with the exception of the column $b_1 \ldots b_n$), should be equal to zero. If the rank is *exactly* $(n-2)$, which implies that there is in (a) at least one non-zero determinant of order $(n-2)$, the afore-mentioned necessary condition is also sufficient. Thus it is possible to choose in some way two variables, such that all the other variables can be expressed as linear functions of these, and that the corresponding $(x_1 \ldots x_n)$ satisfy all the equations (8.15) whatever values are assigned to the two selected variables. In other words, we have a solution system with two degrees of freedom. Not only does this solution system incorporating two arbitrary parameters exist but, once constructed, it generates all the solutions of (8.15).

When the rank of the matrix (a) is r, the general solution incorporates $(n-r)$ arbitrary parameters.

Hence the following theorem.

THEOREM (8.30). If a system of linear equations of the form (8.15) has a coefficient-matrix (a) whose rank is *less* than n, and if there exists a solution-system $(x_1 \ldots x_n)$, then there also exists a solution system where *not* all the $x_1 \ldots x_n$ are simultaneously zero. (This theorem is false if the rank of (a) is equal to n.)

72

The completely general criterion for solvability will be formulated later, in (8.37). Before coming to that, we shall mention an application which is directly connected with theorem (8.30). One can confirm easily that in the case when the rank of (a) is $(n-1)$, a *homogeneous* system (i.e. when $b_1 = b_2 = \ldots = b_n = 0$) always satisfies the condition of solvability whatever the values of the elements a_{ij}. This is also true in the general case when the rank of (a) is an arbitrary number less than n. Thus we can formulate the following theorem.

THEOREM (8.31). A *homogeneous* system of linear equations which has the same number of equations as unknowns, and whose coefficient matrix (a) is of rank *less* than n, always has a solution system. Among the solutions one can find a solution system where not all the $x_1 \ldots x_n$ are simultaneously zero. (This is a generalisation of (8.27).)

Definition of a general linear system with m equations and n unknowns. Fundamental theorems concerning the existence of solutions of a general system

Let us attempt now to formulate a completely general criterion of solvability. For this purpose, we consider the case when the number of equations is not n but a number m, which can be equal to, greater than, or less than n. Theorem (8.34) states a necessary and sufficient condition for the existence of a solution; theorem (8.37) describes the nature of the solution.

We consider a system of equations of the form

$$
\begin{aligned}
a_{11}x_1 + a_{12}x_2 + \cdots + a_{1n}x_n &= b_1 \\
a_{21}x_1 + a_{22}x_2 + \cdots + a_{2n}x_n &= b_2 \\
&\cdots\cdots\cdots\cdots \\
a_{m1}x_1 + a_{m2}x_2 + \cdots + a_{mn}x_n &= b_m
\end{aligned}
$$

(8.32)

or, more briefly

(8.33)
$$
\sum_k a_{hk}x_k = b_h \qquad (h = 1, 2, \ldots m).
$$

THEOREM (8.34). A necessary and sufficient condition for the existence of a system of (finite) numbers $x_1 \ldots x_n$ satisfying (8.32) with given coefficients a and b is that the *matrix of the left-hand* side

(8.35)

$$\begin{Vmatrix} a_{11}a_{12} \ldots a_{1n} \\ a_{21}a_{22} \ldots a_{2n} \\ \cdots\cdots\cdots\cdots \\ a_{m1}a_{m2} \ldots a_{mn} \end{Vmatrix}$$

and the *complete matrix*

(8.36)

$$\begin{Vmatrix} a_{11}a_{12} \ldots a_{1n}b_1 \\ a_{21}a_{22} \ldots a_{2n}b_2 \\ \cdots\cdots\cdots\cdots\cdots \\ a_{m1}a_{m2} \ldots a_{mn}b_m \end{Vmatrix}$$

should have the same rank.

THEOREM (8.37). If the conditions formulated in (8.34) are fulfilled and if the common rank of (8.35) and (8.36) is r, there exists at least one way of choosing a set of $(n-r)$ variables – called the basis – such that the other r variables can be expressed as linear functions of the $(n-r)$ variables of the aforementioned basis, and in such a way that $(x_1 \ldots x_n)$ satisfies the m equations (8.33), whatever the values (zero or not) assigned to the $(n-r)$ variables of the basis.

The linear forms indicating how the r variables depend on the $(n-r)$ variables of the basis are found by choosing in (8.35) a non-zero sub-determinant of order r (there exists at least one such sub-determinant if (8.35) is of rank r) and considering the corresponding equations of (8.33) as a system of r equations in r unknowns. This system can be solved uniquely, since the determinant of the coefficients of the left-hand side is not zero.

For each non-zero determinant of rank r of (8.35), one can thus construct a basis of $(n-r)$ arbitrary variables. Moreover, if the $(n-r)$ variables of the basis vary freely, any one of these bases gives rise to all the solutions of (8.33).

We shall not give the proof of theorems (8.34) and (8.37). We confine ourselves to noting that it is confirmed by *all the examples* mentioned above.

Case of non-zero solutions

On the basis of the preceding discussion we can state the following theorem.

THEOREM (8.38). In every case when the system of equations of the form (8.32) has a solution it has also a solution where not all the $x_1 \dots x_n$ are simultaneously zero, with the exception of the case when the system under consideration reduces to a homogeneous system and the matrix (8.35) is of rank n; in this last case, all the variables occurring on the left-hand side of the system are necessarily zero.

The following observation confirms the correctness of (8.38).

In the case when $\|a\|$ is of rank less than n, the solution has one or more degrees of freedom, and consequently at least one of the unknowns of the equations can be chosen arbitrarily – and thus, if one so wishes, it can be chosen to be different from zero. But in the case when the rank of $\|a\|$ is n, the solution is determined uniquely. And if the system is homogeneous all the unknowns will be necessarily zero. If the solution consists of zeros only, the right-hand terms – which are linear forms of the unknowns – will also consist of zeros only. Thus, if $\|a\|$ is of rank n, the solution will be identically zero if and only if the system is homogeneous.

The process derived from theorem (8.37), which consists of choosing directly $(n-r)$ variables of (8.33) as parameters providing the solution, is not the only one which leads to the solution of the general problem. There exist several other methods, for example the method described as "by projection" which is expedient in certain circumstances, but which we will not discuss here.

General theorems concerning homogeneous systems

In the case when the system (8.32) is *homogeneous*, that is when all the *b*-s are zero, the condition stated by the theorem (8.34) is always fulfilled. In fact, the matrix formed from (8.35) by adjoining a column consisting exclusively of zeros cannot have a rank different from the rank of (8.35) itself. Hence the following theorem.

THEOREM (8.39). A system of homogeneous linear equations has always at least one solution irrespective whether the number of equations is greater than, equal to or less than the number of unknowns.

Theorem (8.39) follows immediately if we include $x_1 = x_2 = \dots = x_n = 0$ among the solutions. We can obviously do this if the question is only whether or not there exists a solution and if we do not assume in advance that this solution must have certain properties. Hence, if one admits solutions where all the $(x_1 \ldots x_n)$ are identically zero, the correctness of the theorem is evident, since any homogeneous system of linear equations will be satisfied by $x_1 = x_2 = \ldots = x_n = 0$.

However, the question which often is of interest when dealing with linear equations is to know whether or not there exists a solution whose components $x_1, x_2, \ldots, x_n$, are *not* all identically zero. This question is answered by the following theorem.

THEOREM (8.40). A necessary and sufficient condition for a *homogeneous* system of equations to have a solution where the unknowns are *not* all identically zero is that the rank of the coefficient matrix should be less than the number of unknowns, irrespective of the fact whether the system has more, less, or the same number of equations as unknowns. (This is a generalisation of (8.31).)

The following observation confirms the correctness of theorem (8.40).

The rank of a homogeneous system can never exceed the number of equations. If the rank is equal to the number of unknowns: n, we can take n equations in such a way that the determinant of the system formed in this way is not zero. It follows then from (8.19) that all the unknowns will be zero. On the other hand, if the rank of the system of equations is less than n, then, in virtue of the theorems (8.39) and (8.37), there exists a solution where at least one of the unknowns can be chosen arbitrarily, that is, if it is desired, can be chosen to be different from zero.

EXAMPLES

Linear equations

We will attempt to show in our examples how the various circumstances encountered in the study of these equations correspond effectively to very concrete economic situations.

EXAMPLE (8.1′)

Introduction

Let us consider a very simplified economy with two categories of goods a and b, and a single category of perfectly homogeneous man-power u – this category of labourers being also at the same time considered as the single, perfectly homogeneous, category of consumers.

We are going to see that, by varying the hypotheses on the utilisation of goods, we shall encounter the principal situations studied abstractly in the text, and in consequence, gradually we shall be led to use the different theorems which we have stated in Chapter VIII.

CHAPTER VIII

In a general way we shall suppose that the production of one unit of

a absorbs   5   units of man-power u
0.2 units of preexistent a
0.7 units of preexistent b

b absorbs   5   units of man-power u
0.7 units of preexistent a
0.1 units of preexistent b

and that the man-power available in the course of the period considered exists in a quantity u_0.

The start of the production process is made possible by means of appropriate initial stocks of a and b.

Under these conditions, if during the period one could produce

$$\lambda \text{ units of } a$$

and

$$\mu \text{ units of } b$$

these quantities need respectively as inputs:

for λ of a:	for μ of b:	altogether:
5 λ of u	5 μ of u	$5(\lambda + \mu)$ of u
0.2 λ of a	0.7 μ of a	$0.2\lambda + 0.7\mu$ of a
0.7 λ of b	0.1 μ of b	$0.7\lambda + 0.1\mu$ of b

Thus, the volumes of the available quantities of a and b – which we consider in the standing arrangement as the only utilisable quantities – at the end of the production-period amount to

$$\lambda - [0.2\lambda + 0.7\mu] \text{ of } a = \quad 0.8\lambda - 0.7\mu \text{ of } a$$
$$\mu - [0.7\lambda + 0.1\mu] \text{ of } b = -0.7\lambda + 0.9\mu \text{ of } b$$

Moreover it is clear that to produce the optimal quantities of a and b, one has to utilise all the available man-power, whatever the utilization of the products may be.

This gives us $5(\lambda + \mu) = u_0$

(1) We shall assume now that while a is indispensable for the production of b, only b is utilized for consumption. Thus it is clear that we have no interest in accumulating a, and that it is best to reserve the man-power as much as possible for the production of b, and to produce only as much of a as is needed for the production of b.

In the standing arrangement considered we will keep the volume of the available quantity of a to zero, which gives us the condition $0.8\lambda - 0.7\mu = 0$ which, together with the relation $5(\lambda + \mu) = u_0$, forming together the System S_1 will determine λ and μ.

It is clear that the solution of S_1 in no way requires us to employ the theory of Chapter VIII. The first equation gives:

$$\lambda = \frac{7}{8}\mu$$

and substituting this into the second:

$$5\left(\frac{7}{8}\mu + \mu\right) = u_0 \quad \text{or} \quad \frac{75}{8}\mu = u_0.$$

Hence

$$\begin{cases} \mu = \dfrac{8}{75} u_0 \\[2ex] \lambda = \dfrac{7}{8}\dfrac{8}{75} u_0 = \dfrac{7}{75} u_0. \end{cases}$$

Thus the available quantity of b is

$$0.9\,\mu - 0.7\,\lambda = \frac{7.2 - 4.9}{75} u_0 = \frac{2.3}{75} u_0.$$

Extension to a more complex economy

We can generalize by extending this simple example to a case which conceptually is entirely analogous, but which – because of the large number of variables involved – requires the utilisation of the theory of linear equations given in Chapter VIII.

This example will concern a sector of industry B, which is sufficiently integrated to be considered as isolated and self-sufficient with respect to its production process but not with respect to the market of its product. B produces the goods $a_1, a_2, ..., a_p$ in quantities $\lambda_1, \lambda_2, ..., \lambda_p$, which are used only for the production of a final product a_n (in quantity μ) of which the available stock is sold. If one assumes that B needs specialized man-power of which only a quantity u_0 exists, and which is utilised in its entirety, it is clear that B has an interest in maximising the production of a_n, and in eliminating the volume of the stocks of $a_1, a_2, ..., a_p$.

If now C_{ij} is the quantity of a_i used for the production of one unit of the commodity a_j, the production of λ_j units of a_j requires $\lambda_j C_{1j}$ of a_1, $\lambda_j C_{2j}$ of a_2, ..., $\lambda_j C_{ij}$ of a_i, ..., $\lambda_j C_{nj}$ of a_n and the production of μ units of a_n requires μC_{1n} of a_1, μC_{2n} of a_2, ..., μC_{in} of a_i, ..., μC_{nn} of a_n. Thus the total amount of a_i used up in the manufacture will be

$$\lambda_1 C_{i1} + \lambda_2 C_{i2} + \cdots + \lambda_j C_{ij} + \cdots + \lambda_p C_{ip} + \mu C_{in}$$

and the surplus quantity of a_i will be

$$\lambda_i - [\lambda_1 C_{i1} + \lambda_2 C_{i2} + \cdots + \lambda_i C_{ii} + \cdots + \lambda_j C_{ij} + \cdots + \lambda_p C_{ip} + \mu C_{in}] = d_i$$

where

$$d_i = -\lambda_1 C_{i1} - \lambda_2 C_{i2} - \cdots + \lambda_i [1 - C_{ii}] - \cdots - \lambda_j C_{ij} \cdots - \lambda_p C_{ip} - \mu C_{in}$$

Thus we must have for $i = 1, 2, ..., p$,

$$d_i = 0$$

that is, we have p equations

$$-\lambda_1 C_{i1} - \lambda_2 C_{i2} - \cdots + \lambda_i [1 - C_{ii}] \cdots - \lambda_j C_{ij} \cdots - \lambda_p C_{ip} - \mu C_{in} = 0$$

and if u_i is the man-power used up for the manufacture of each unit of a_i, we also must have

$$\lambda_1 u_1 + \lambda_2 u_2 + \cdots + \lambda_i u_i + \cdots + \lambda_p u_p + \mu u_n = u_0$$

78

It is now clear that we can solve or discuss such a system only with the help of the theory expounded in Chapter VIII. We leave it to the reader to solve as an exercise the following numerical system with a given table of coefficients:

The utilised quantity of:

For each unit of	a_1	a_2	a_3	a_4	a_n	u_0
a_1	0.1	0.1	0.1	0.1	0	0.1
a_2	0.1	0.2	0.1	0.1	0	0.1
a_3	0.1	0.1	0.2	0.1	0	0.1
a_4	0.1	0.1	0.1	0.2	0	0.1
a_n	0.1	0.1	0.1	0.1	0	0.1

The reader will find the rates of manufacture to be as follows

For

$$a_1: \quad u_0$$

$$a_2: \quad \frac{10}{9} u_0$$

$$a_3: \quad \frac{10}{9} u_0$$

$$a_4: \quad \frac{10}{9} u_0$$

$$a_n: \quad \frac{17 \, u_0}{3}.$$

(2) Let us return to our simple example of two goods a and b which we have defined in the introduction, but this time we will assume that a and b are consumed by the man-power (Labour force) in a homogeneous way, each unit of the man-power consuming k units of a and l units of b (k and l being constants). In a real economy, progressing at an appreciably constant rate, it is not absurd to assume that consumer habits are such that all the available units of a and b are consumed.

Thus one has

$$\left. \begin{array}{l} 5\,(\lambda + \mu) = \quad u_0 \\ 0.8\,\lambda - 0.7\,\mu = ku_0 \\ -0.7\,\lambda + 0.9\,\mu = lu_0 \end{array} \right\} S_2$$

Since the quantities of a and b necessary for the consumption are given *a priori* by the last two equations of S_2, there is no reason why the first equation should be satisfied. It would not be difficult to calculate λ and μ from the last two equations, and to substitute these values into the first one to see if it is satisfied, or rather to find the condition which k and l must satisfy (u_0 will disappear because of the homogeneity) in order that the first equation should be fulfilled.

But even here it is more advantageous to apply theorem (8.34) to S_2, considered a system in λ and μ. The left-hand side has the coefficient matrix

$$\left\| \begin{array}{cc} 5 & 5 \\ +0.8 & -0.7 \\ -0.7 & +0.9 \end{array} \right\|$$

This matrix is obviously of rank 2. Thus, S_2 will not be possible unless the matrix

$$\left\| \begin{array}{ccc} 5 & 5 & u_0 \\ 0.8 & -0.7 & ku_0 \\ -0.7 & 0.9 & lu_0 \end{array} \right\|$$

is also of rank 2, which gives the necessary and sufficient condition,

$$\left| \begin{array}{ccc} 5 & 5 & u_0 \\ 0.8 & -0.7 & ku_0 \\ -0.7 & 0.9 & lu_0 \end{array} \right| = 0$$

or, since u_0 is by its nature different from zero

$$\left| \begin{array}{ccc} 5 & 5 & 1 \\ 0.8 & -0.7 & k \\ -0.7 & 0.9 & l \end{array} \right| = 0$$

The calculation gives

$$0.23 = 7.5\,l + 8\,k$$

Strictly speaking, it remains to make sure that (a very frequent economic condition), for given positive values of k and l, the solutions λ and μ are positive or zero. We will not insist on this point.

Another method. We could deal with this example by applying theorem 8.40. In fact, it is clear that the system S_2 is homogeneous with respect to u_0 if it has solutions. In particular, λ and μ are zero if u_0 is zero; except perhaps if the matrix of the left-hand side is of rank less than two (which is not the case). Moreover, it is clear that two unknowns cannot be zero without the third one also being zero. Under these conditions if we consider S_2 this time as a homogeneous system $\bar{S}_2$ in three unknowns λ, μ, and u_0, a solution of S_2 corresponds to a solution of $\bar{S}_2$ where u_0 in particular is not zero. Conversely, if $\bar{S}_2$ has non-zero solutions, the value of u_0 – as we have seen – cannot be zero. By the proportionality we can assign to u_0 in $\bar{S}_2$ its known value in S_2, and we can say definitely that $\bar{S}_2$ has non-zero solutions. In view of theorem 9.40, this can be expressed by the fact that the matrix

$$\left\| \begin{array}{ccc} 5 & 5 & 1 \\ 0.8 & -0.7 & k \\ -0.7 & 0.9 & l \end{array} \right\|$$

is of rank strictly less than 3, which gives us the necessary and sufficient condition we have already found earlier, that the determinant of the matrix

$$\left| \begin{array}{ccc} 5 & 5 & 1 \\ 0.8 & -0.7 & k \\ -0.7 & 0.9 & l \end{array} \right| = 0$$

(3) This example will be a simple generalization of (8.1') (2). To bring about the transition, we shall consider an economic system of the type described at the end of (8.1') (1), but with a well-determined number of products, say, five – a_1, a_2, a_3; b_1 b_2 – of which only the last two – b_1 and b_2 – are used for consumption. Further, we shall assume that there are two categories of man-power u and v, available in quantities u_0 and v_0, and that each unit of u consumes k_1 units of b_1 and l_1 units of b_2 respectively, and each unit of v consumes k_2 units of b_1 and l_2 units of b_2.

Furthermore, the following table gives the use of the products as inputs into the various production processes.

Utilisation of units of the products

for each unit produced of	a_1	a_2	a_3	b_1	b_2	u	v
a_1	0.1	0.2	0.1	0	0	1	0.1
a_2	0.2	0.2	0.3	0	0	1	0.3
a_3	0.1	0.1	0.1	0	0	0.8	0.1
b_1	0	0.2	0.3	0.1	0.2	0.8	0.1
b_2	0.1	0	0	0.2	0.3	0	0.4

If the goods a_1, a_2, a_3; b_1, b_2 are produced in the quantities λ_1, λ_2, λ_3; μ_1, μ_2 respectively, we shall have the following equations:

System S_3	
Equations for the utilisation of the intermediate products a_1, a_2, a_3: three equations (one for each intermediate product)	$0.9\,\lambda_1 - 0.2\,\lambda_2 - 0.1\,\lambda_3 - 0.1\,\mu_2 = 0$ $-0.2\,\lambda_1 + 0.8\,\lambda_2 - 0.1\,\lambda_3 - 0.2\,\mu_1 = 0$ $-0.1\,\lambda_1 - 0.3\,\lambda_2 + 0.9\,\lambda_3 - 0.3\,\mu_1 = 0$
Equations for the utilisation of the available quantities of the consumption-goods: two equations (one for each good b) independently of the number of different man-powers.	$0.9\,\mu_1 - 0.2\,\mu_2 = k_1 u_0 + k_2 v_0$ $-0.2\,\mu_1 + 0.7\,\mu_2 = l_1 u_0 + l_2 v_0$
Finally, the equations for the employment of the man-power: two equations (one for each type of man-power, independently of the number of products.	$\lambda_1 + \lambda_2 + 0.8\,\lambda_3 + 0.8\,\mu_1 = u_0$ $0.1\,\lambda_1 + 0.3\,\lambda_2 + 0.1\,\lambda_3 + 0.1\,\mu_1 + 0.4\,\mu_2 = v_0$

To study the conditions of compatibility for this system S_3, we will apply theorem (8-37). It is sufficient to require that the matrix C of the left-hand side coefficients, i.e.

81

5 columns: 1 for each unknown $\lambda_1, \lambda_2, \lambda_3, \mu_1, \mu_2$

7 rows:	0.9	− 0.2	− 0.1	0	− 0.1
one for each	− 0.2	0.8	− 0.1	− 0.2	0
equation	− 0.1	− 0.3	0.9	− 0.3	0
C	0	0	0	0.9	− 0.2
	0	0	0	− 0.2	0.7
	1	1	0.8	0.8	0
	0.1	0.3	0.1	0.1	0.4

and the matrix completed by the column of right-hand terms, say T:

6 columns: 5 for the unknowns, plus one for the right-hand side

Always 7 rows,	0.9	− 0.2	− 0.1	0	− 0.1	0
one for each	− 0.2	0.8	− 0.1	− 0.2	0	0
equation	− 0.1	− 0.3	0.9	− 0.3	0	0
T	0	0	0	0.9	− 0.2	$k_1 u_0 + k_2 v_0$
	0	0	0	− 0.2	0.7	$l_1 u_0 + l_2 v_0$
	1	1	0.8	0.8	0	u_0
	0.1	0.3	0.1	0.1	0.4	v_0

should have the same rank.

It is easy to see that C is effectively of rank 5 (for example by taking the determinant D, consisting of the five first rows of the matrix). We leave it to the reader to calculate this determinant; its value is $+ 10^{-5}$ (59 × 569).

Thus we must verify that T is also of rank 5, i.e. not of rank 6. In the present state of our knowledge, it would now seem necessary to verify that all the determinants of order 6 extracted from T (there are 7 of these) are zero. In fact (and this is true in general), it is sufficient to consider the two determinants which contain all the 5 rows of C (whose known determinant is the non-zero D): the first one constructed from the first five and the sixth row of T, the second one from the first five and the seventh row. To see that one can in fact limit oneself to verifying that these two determinants are zero, it is only necessary to imagine that one has solved the first five equations of S_3, which can be done in a unique way, since the matrix of the coefficients of the unknowns of these equations is of the maximal rank 5 (in fact, its determinant is $D \neq 0$), and is thus of the same rank as the matrix completed by the column of known right-hand sides. Thus, it is sufficient to substitute these solutions first into the sixth, and then into the seventh equation, and to verify that these are satisfied. It is quite clear that it suffices to apply theorem (8.37) twice, once for the first five and the sixth equation, and a second time for the first five and the seventh equation.

This consideration gives us the necessary and sufficient conditions which must be satisfied by the numerically undetermined values of $u_0, v_0, k_1, l_1, k_2, l_2$. These conditions are of the form

$$T_1 \begin{vmatrix} 0.9 & -0.2 & -0.1 & 0 & -0.1 & 0 \\ -0.2 & 0.8 & -0.1 & -0.2 & 0 & 0 \\ -0.1 & -0.3 & 0.9 & -0.3 & 0 & 0 \\ 0 & 0 & 0 & 0.9 & -0.2 & (k_1 u_0 + k_2 v_0) \\ 0 & 0 & 0 & -0.2 & 0.7 & (l_1 u_0 + l_2 v_0) \\ 1 & 1 & 0.8 & 0.8 & 0 & u_0 \end{vmatrix} = 0$$

and

$$T_2 \begin{vmatrix} 0.9 & -0.2 & -0.1 & 0 & -0.1 & 0 \\ -0.2 & 0.8 & -0.1 & -0.2 & 0 & 0 \\ -0.1 & -0.3 & 0.9 & -0.3 & 0 & 0 \\ 0 & 0 & 0 & 0.9 & -0.2 & (k_1u_0 + k_2v_0) \\ 0 & 0 & 0 & -0.2 & 0.7 & (l_1u_0 + l_2v_0) \\ 0.1 & 0.3 & 0.1 & 0.1 & 0.4 & v_0 \end{vmatrix} = 0$$

The condition T_1 can be written for example as

$$[k_1u_0 + k_2v_0] \begin{vmatrix} 0.9 & -0.2 & -0.1 & 0 & -0.1 \\ -0.2 & 0.8 & -0.1 & -0.2 & 0 \\ -0.1 & -0.3 & 0.9 & -0.3 & 0 \\ 0 & 0 & 0 & -0.2 & 0.7 \\ 1 & 1 & 0.8 & 0.8 & 0 \end{vmatrix}$$

$$- [l_1u_0 + l_2v_0] \begin{vmatrix} 0.9 & -0.2 & -0.1 & 0 & -0.1 \\ -0.2 & 0.8 & -0.1 & -0.2 & 0 \\ -0.1 & -0.3 & 0.9 & -0.3 & 0 \\ 0 & 0 & 0 & 0.9 & -0.2 \\ 1 & 1 & 0.8 & 0.8 & 0 \end{vmatrix}$$

$$+ u_0 \begin{vmatrix} & & D \text{ (already calculated)} & & \\ & & & & \end{vmatrix} = 0$$

The condition T_2 can be written in an analogous form and we leave it to the reader to write down the conditions explicitly. For his guidance, we may say that he should find

$$T_1 \equiv -0.67070\,(k_1u_0 + k_2v_0) - 0.27524\,(l_1u_0 + l_2v_0) + 0.33571\,u_0 = 0$$
$$T_2 \equiv -0.15206\,(k_1u_0 + k_2v_0) - 0.24708\,(l_1u_0 + l_2v_0) + 0.33571\,v_0 = 0$$

Such an example as the one given here may appear rather artificial. It is clear in fact that it is contrary to observation to imagine that the consumptions of the man-powers u and v *must* be equal to the fixed amounts b_1 and b_2. It is more logical to search for conditions under which these consumptions will be between given upper and lower bounds. Such conditions would replace many of our equalities by inequalities. Thus we would be faced with a problem in linear programming (cf. Chapter 2). However, on the one hand such a problem would involve, among others, the theory of linear equations, and on the other hand the general treatment we have given to these examples (8.1′) is capable of perfectly reasonable economic interpretations. If one makes the very plausible assumption of full employment, we shall determine the progress of production by solving the three first and the two last equations of the system S_3. This done, the fourth and fifth equations will indicate the conditions which must be satisfied by the rules of consumption in order that the available products should be entirely absorbed by the market. Now, while in this new economic interpretation which we have indicated, the order of solution is different from what we have done previously, it still simply amounts to asserting that the system S_3 has a solution. This is exactly the problem which has been dealt with in our example, and which leads us to the conditions T_1 and T_2 which in our new line of reasoning acquire a more normal economic interpretation. Developing this interpretation one can thus easily imagine for example – assuming less rigid habits of consumption than we have done before – that one attempts to regulate the prices and salaries in such a way that all the products should be sold out. Analytically, this is expressed precisely by the fulfilment of the conditions T_1 and T_2. One can also imagine other natural conditions which make use in one way or another of the conditions T_1 and T_2 for the solvability of S_3.

Summary of the results concerning linear equations in two unknowns

We can sum up the results concerning equations in two unknowns in the following form (cases (I), (II) and (III) correspond to the three principal cases considered at the beginning of the present chapter):

Let

I.
$$\begin{vmatrix} a_{11}a_{12} \\ a_{21}a_{22} \end{vmatrix} \neq 0.$$

In this case, there always is one and only one solution, (x_1, x_2), whatever the values of b_1 and b_2. If the two numbers b_1 and b_2 are zero, the two numbers x_1 and x_2 will also be zero. Moreover, if at least one of the numbers b_1 and b_2 is not zero, at least one of the numbers x_1 and x_2 will be necessarily different from zero.

Let

II.
$$\begin{vmatrix} a_{11}a_{12} \\ a_{21}a_{22} \end{vmatrix} = 0$$

and let at least one of the determinants

$$\begin{vmatrix} b_1 a_{12} \\ b_2 a_{22} \end{vmatrix} \quad \text{and} \quad \begin{vmatrix} a_{11} b_1 \\ a_{21} b_2 \end{vmatrix} \neq 0.$$

In this case there exists no (finite) solution (x_1, x_2).

Let

III.
$$\begin{vmatrix} a_{11}a_{12} \\ a_{21}a_{22} \end{vmatrix} = 0$$

and

$$\begin{vmatrix} b_1 a_{12} \\ b_2 a_{22} \end{vmatrix} = \begin{vmatrix} a_{11} b_1 \\ a_{21} b_2 \end{vmatrix} = 0.$$

84

In this case, there will or will not exist a solution according to whether or not these conditions are joined by certain other conditions. We can distinguish the following possibilities:

(A). At least one of the four elements of the matrix

$$\begin{pmatrix} a_{11}a_{12} \\ a_{21}a_{22} \end{pmatrix}$$

is not zero. In this case, there always exists a solution (x_1, x_2) and this solution has one degree of freedom. At least one of the two unknowns x_1 and x_2 can be chosen arbitrarily (non-zero if we wish). The other unknown is determined as a function of the first one.

(B). The four elements of the matrix

$$\begin{pmatrix} a_{11}a_{12} \\ a_{21}a_{22} \end{pmatrix}$$

are all zero, and one of the numbers b_1 and b_2 is non-zero.

In this case, there is no (finite) solution (x_1, x_2).

(C) The four elements of the matrix

$$\begin{pmatrix} a_{11}a_{12} \\ a_{21}a_{22} \end{pmatrix}$$

and the numbers b_1 and b_2 are all zero.

In this case, there exists a solution (x_1, x_2) and this solution has two degrees of freedom. Both unknowns x_1 and x_2 can be defined arbitrarily (we can take one or both to be non-zero if we wish).

One sees that the three sub-cases ranged under the principal case (III) are of the same nature as the three principal cases (I), (II), and (III) themselves. The situation is the same for systems of equations in several unknowns. Thus the cases are divided into several "stages", in such a manner that it is always possible to distinguish three cases analogous to (I), (II), and (III), of which the last one can itself be divided into the three "subcases".

LINEAR RELATIONS BETWEEN VECTORS, BETWEEN FUNCTIONS, AND BETWEEN EQUATIONS

Definition of a 'vector' and a 'system of vectors'

A set of n numbers can be represented in the form of a *point* in n-dimensional space, accepting that it is written with respect to n mutually perpendicular coordinate axes. For $n=1$, we have simply a point of the axis; for $n=2$, we have a point of a plane; for $n=3$, we have a point of the space, as for example the point A of figure (9.1), where (1), (2), (3)

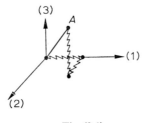

Fig. (9.1)

denote the axes. If $n>3$, the term "space" is nothing more than a convenient expression, but this terminology is very suitable for a clear understanding of a number of facts.

Instead of considering the *point* in question, we can also consider the segment joining the origin to the point. This segment is called a *vector*, and the coordinates of the point are referred to as the components of the vector. By considering the vector rather than the point, one often obtains a clearer and more intuitive representation. That is what we shall do here.

Let us consider m vectors joining the origin to m different points of the space. We call this set a *system of vectors*.

Let $(v_1) (v_2) \dots (v_m)$ be the symbols of m vectors. We can write the components in the form of a matrix

(9.2)
$$\begin{Vmatrix} v_{11}v_{12} \cdots v_{1n} \\ v_{21}v_{22} \cdots v_{2n} \\ \cdots\cdots\cdots\cdots \\ v_{m1}v_{m2} \cdots v_{mn} \end{Vmatrix}$$

v_{ij} is j-th component of the i-th vector. The first row of (9.2) gives the components of the first vector, the second row the components of the second vector, etc.

We shall now discuss the various situations which may arise in connection with a system of vectors.

Linear dependence of two vectors

If the components of (v_2) – i.e. the numbers given by the second row of (9.2) – are proportional to the components of (v_1) – i.e. the numbers given by the first row of (9.2) – we say that the two vectors (v_1) and (v_2) are linearly dependent, which is expressed by saying that there exist two numbers μ_1 and μ_2 (not simultaneously zero) such that

(9.3) $$\mu_1 v_{1j} + \mu_2 v_{2j} = 0 \quad \text{for all} \quad j = 1, 2 \ldots n.$$

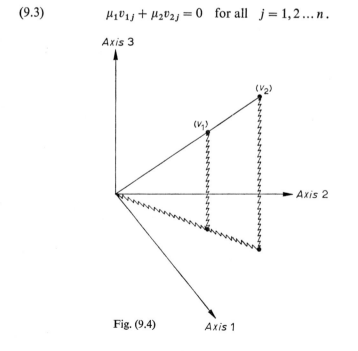

Fig. (9.4)

The two numbers μ_1 and μ_2 – if they exist – are clearly determined but for a factor of proportionality. The geometric representation of the situation when (9.3) is satisfied shows the two vectors (v_1) and (v_2) on the same straight line passing through the origin, as is shown in figure (9.4).

Graphical representation and mathematical expression of the linear dependence of three vectors

We say that the three vectors (v_1), (v_2) and (v_3) are linearly dependent if there exist three numbers μ_1, μ_2, μ_3, not all zero such that

(9.5) $$\mu_1 v_{1j} + \mu_2 v_{2j} + \mu_3 v_{3j} = 0 \quad \text{for all} \quad j = 1, 2 \ldots n.$$

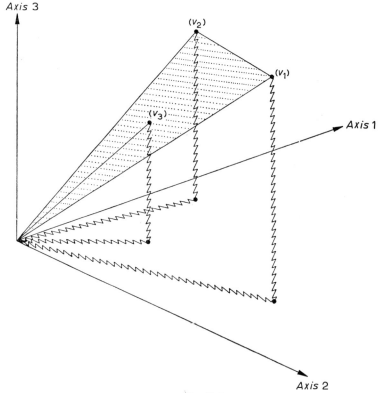

Fig. (9.6)

In this case it is again clear that if there exist three numbers μ_1, μ_2, μ_3 answering this definition these will only be determined but for a factor of proportionality. We shall have a geometric representation of the situation (9.5) if we imagine that the three vectors (v_1), (v_2), (v_3) all lie in the same plane, or if one of the three vectors happens to lie in the plane *generated* by the other two. This is shown by figure (9.6).

Linear dependence of m vectors

In general, we say that the m vectors defined by (9.2) are *linearly dependent* if there exist m numbers μ_1, μ_2, ..., μ_m, not all zero, such that,

$$(9.7) \qquad \mu_1 v_{1j} + \mu_2 v_{2j} + \cdots + \mu_m v_{mj} = 0 \quad \text{for all} \quad j = 1, 2, \ldots n.$$

In the opposite case, we say that the m vectors (v_1) ... (v_n) are *linearly independent*. The notions of linear dependence and independence are very important for various problems.

If we look upon the expression (9.7) for a moment as a system of linear equations with respect to the m numbers $(\mu_1 \ldots \mu_m)$, the theory of linear equations tells us that such a non-identically zero solution can exist only if the matrix (9.2) is of rank *less than m*.

When the matrix (9.2) is of rank $R\,(< m)$, we say that the m vectors $(v_1) \ldots (v_n)$ are $(m-R)$ times linearly dependent. There exists an *R-dimensional space* which *contains* all the vectors. Thus, we also say that these vectors have an unfolding capacity sufficient to unfold an R-dimensional space. For example, the three vectors of the figure (9.6) have the unfolding capacity sufficient to unfold a 2-dimensional space since all three are in a plane. If it is only a question of generating this plane, it is sufficient to consider two of the three vectors. Later on we give a more detailed discussion on the connection existing between the notion of the unfolding capacity of a system of vectors and that of linear relations between equations.

We can express the meaning of the rank R of (9.2) algebraically by saying that if (9.2) is of rank R, and only then, there exists a set of values $(\mu_1 \ldots \mu_m)$ having $(m-R)$ degrees of freedom which satisfies (9.7). The m values $(\mu_1 \ldots \mu_m)$ can be expressed linearly by means of $(m-R)$ arbitrary parameters in such a way that (9.7) is satisfied whatever the values of these parameters.

Another way to express this situation is to say that if the rank of (9.2) is R, it is always possible to choose somehow a *basis of R vectors*, such that all the other $(m-R)$ vectors are linear functions of the first R vectors. To say that a vector is a linear function of other vectors, is the same as to say that each component of the vector is a linear combination of the corresponding components of the other vectors, the coefficients of these combinations being independent of the chosen component. In other words, if (9.2) is of rank R, it is possible to choose, at least in one way, a basis of R vectors – for example $v_{(1)}, v_{(2)}, ..., v_{(R)}$ – such that we have symbolically

(9.8)
$$(v_h) = c_{h1}(v_1) + c_{h2}(v_2) + \cdots + c_{hR}(v_R)$$
$$\text{for } h = R+1, R+2, ..., m,$$

where

$$c_{hk} \left(\begin{matrix} h = R+1, R+2, ..., m \\ k = 1, 2, ..., R \end{matrix} \right)$$

are the multipliers.

Equation (9.8) means that the corresponding equation expressed in terms of the components is true for every component, without modifying the numbers c_{hk}. Thus, we have

(9.9) $$v_{hj} = c_{h1}v_{1j} + c_{h2}v_{2j} + \cdots + c_{hR}v_{Rj} \quad \left(\begin{matrix} h = R+1, R+2, ..., m \\ j = 1, 2, ..., n \end{matrix} \right)$$

The equations (9.8)–(9.9) are represented geometrically by the figure (9.6), where one has $R=2$, $m=3$, $n=3$. We can choose two vectors lying in the shaded plane; this done, we can express the third vector as a linear function of the two others. We could not do this if the three vectors were *dissociated*, and not situated in the same plane.

The following argument will show that, if (9.2) is of rank R, there always exists a relation of the type (9.9). It follows from the theory of linear equations that if we look upon (9.7) as a homogeneous system of linear equations, and if (9.2) is of rank $R\,(<m)$, there always exists a solution $(\mu_1 ... \mu_m)$ in which $(m-R)$ of the $(\mu_1 ... \mu_m)$ can be chosen arbitrarily, and the remaining R of the $(\mu_1 ... \mu_m)$ are determined linear combinations of the afore-mentioned $(m-R)$ values. Since we can choose our notation, we can assume that the values which can be defined arbitrarily are the last $(m-R)$, that is, $\mu_{R+1}, \mu_{R+2}, ..., \mu_m$.

90

As a first arbitrary choice, we take

(9.10) $\mu_{R+1} = -1$ and $\mu_{R+2} = \mu_{R+3} = \cdots = \mu_m = 0$.

Hence, in virtue of (9.7)

(9.11) $(v_{R+1}) = \mu_1(v_1) + \mu_2(v_2) + \cdots + \mu_R(v_R)$,

or, explicitly,

(9.12) $v_{R+1,j} = \mu_1 v_{1j} + \mu_2 v_{2j} + \cdots + \mu_R v_{Rj}$ for $j = 1, 2, \ldots, n$

This is a linear expression of the type (9.9) for $h = R + 1$.

If we next take as a second arbitrary choice of $(\mu_{R+1}, \mu_{R+2}, \cdots, \mu_m)$ all the values equal to 0, except for $\mu_{R+2} = -1$, we obtain similarly a linear expression of the type (9.9) for $h = R + 2$, and so on.

Linear relations between functions

Let

(9.13) $\varphi_1(t), \varphi_2(t), \ldots, \varphi_m(t)$

be a set of m functions of the variable t. For example, to be more concrete, we can imagine that the variable t represents the time. As an example we could take different polynomials of t. We could also consider functions of several variables. It is of little importance for us to know the domain in which the argument of the function varies (provided it contains "many" points as does, for example, a continuous domain). It is the *number* and the *nature* of the functions $\varphi_1 \ldots \varphi_m$ which is important in what follows.

If there exist m constants $\mu_1 \ldots \mu_m$ not all zero (and independent of t, or more generally, of the variables of $\varphi_1 \ldots \varphi_m$), such that we have

(9.14) $\mu_1 \varphi_1(t) + \mu_2 \varphi_2(t) + \cdots + \mu_m \varphi_m(t) = 0$

identically in t (i.e. for every value of t), we say that the functions $\varphi_1 \ldots \varphi_m$ are *linearly dependent functions* of t. If such numbers $(\mu_1 \ldots \mu_m)$ do not exist, we say that $\varphi_1 \ldots \varphi_m$ are *linearly independent*.

We can use an analogous formulation to express the dependence of functions of several variables.

One sees that the above definitions are analogous to those which we formulated earlier for vectors. The only difference is that in the case of vectors, the "domain of variations" consisted of the n different values of the index j: say $j = 1, 2, ..., n$, while we now have a general domain of variation of the variable t, or possibly of several variables.

It is clear that if the amplitude A, the phase a, and the frequency α are three given numbers, the two functions

$$(9.15) \qquad \varphi_1(t) = A \sin(a + \alpha t) \quad \text{and} \quad \varphi_2(t) = A \cos(a + \alpha t)$$

are linearly independent. But if we add another function $\varphi_3(t)$ in sine and cosine, with the *same* frequency α, the three functions φ_1, φ_2, φ_3 thus obtained will always be linearly dependent. In vector terminology: the three vectors φ_1, φ_2, φ_3 have the unfolding capacity of dimensionality 2 only.

One sees in the same way that any system of functions consisting of powers of t multiplied by arbitrary coefficients will always be linearly independent, provided all the exponents are different.

By an appeal to the fundamental theorems on linear equations and on the linear relations between vectors, one obtains without difficulty a series of important theorems on the subject of functions and their linear relations. Thus, it is easy to prove, for example, that if a polynomial of degree m vanishes for $(m+1)$ values of the argument, then it is identically zero, i.e. zero for *every* value of the argument.

Linear relations between linear equations

Let us now consider linear functions from the point of view of linear dependence. Generally, the situation is the simplest if all the terms are carried to the left. Introducing into the system (8.32) the symbol

$$(9.16) \qquad a_{i0} = -b_i$$

one can write the system in the form

$$(9.17) \qquad
\begin{aligned}
a_{10} + a_{11}x_1 + a_{12}x_2 + \cdots + a_{1n}x_n &= 0 \\
a_{20} + a_{21}x_1 + a_{22}x_2 + \cdots + a_{2n}x_n &= 0 \\
&\cdots\cdots\cdots\cdots\cdots\cdots\cdots\cdots\cdots\cdots \\
a_{m0} + a_{m1}x_1 + a_{m2}x_2 + \cdots + a_{mn}x_n &= 0.
\end{aligned}$$

If all the coefficients of the second equation, i.e. the numbers (a_{20}, a_{21}, ..., a_{2n}), are simply, for example, twice the coefficients (a_{10}, a_{11}, ..., a_{1n}) of the first equation, it is clear that the second does not mean more than the first one. The second equation can be *deduced from the first one*, whatever the values of ($x_1 \ldots x_n$). Every system ($x_1 \ldots x_n$) which satisfies the first equation also satisfies the second. Thus we could just as well suppress the second equation, or else the first one. We say in this case that the two equations are linearly dependent.

There exist other, more complicated, forms of linear relations between equations. Suppose, for example, that the third equation is formed by adding seven times the second equation to five times the first equation. This gives

$$(9.18) \qquad a_{3j} = 5a_{1j} + 7a_{2j}, \quad \text{that is} \quad a_{3j} - 5a_{1j} - 7a_{2j} = 0$$
$$\text{for } j = 0, 1, ..., n.$$

What is of interest to us is that equation (9.18) – with 5 and 7 as fixed coefficients – holds for every value of $j = 0$, 1, ..., n, i.e. for the coefficients of each variable. This being so, obviously we do not change the solutions at all, if we suppress any one of the three first equations.

The line of reasoning will be the same if we take the case where several equations are mutually linearly dependent. In a completely general way, one defines the existence of a linear relation between the equations (9.17), by saying that there exist m numbers $\mu_1 \ldots \mu_m$, not all zero, such that

$$(9.19) \qquad \mu_1 a_{1j} + \mu_2 a_{2j} + \cdots + \mu_m a_{mj} = 0 \quad \text{for} \quad j = 0, 1, ..., n.$$

As one can see, in this way we arrive at a formulation completely analogous to the one we used in connection with linear relations between vectors.

The condition that the ($\mu_1 \ldots \mu_m$) are *not* all zero is important. In fact, if all the ($\mu_1 \ldots \mu_m$) are zero, (9.19) tells nothing about the coefficient matrix (a_{ij}). If at least one of the numbers μ – for example μ_α – is not zero, the α-th equation can be deduced from the others. In fact, we can solve (9.19) with respect to $a_{\alpha j}$ for every j.

We can formulate this statement more clearly by saying that the α-th equation can be deduced from *one or more* of the other equations, according to whether there is one or more non-zero coefficient μ among the remaining coefficients of (9.19). We shall not overlook the case when, with the exception of μ_α, *all* the other coefficients μ of (9.19) are zero. This would mean that all coefficients $(a_{\alpha 0}, a_{\alpha 1}, ..., a_{\alpha n})$ of the α-th equation are zero. Naturally it is convenient to take this extreme case into account if we want to obtain a generally correct formulation of the various criteria. Therefore we will say that an equation with zero coefficients is "linearly dependent on the other equations".

The rank R of the complete matrix of the system of equations. Degree of reduction and degree of freedom

What is the condition for the existence of a system of numbers $(\mu_1 ... \mu_m)$ not all zero, which satisfy (9.19)? The answer is given by theorem (8.40) if (9.19) is considered as a linear system in $(\mu_1 ... \mu_m)$. Clearly the necessary and sufficient condition is that the rank R of the matrix of (9.17) – in other words the rank of the *complete* matrix, in the sense of (8.36) – should be less than m. That is

(9.20) $$R < m.$$

The difference

(9.21) $$P = m - R$$

is called the *degree of reduction* of the system of equations (9.17). We also say that this system is P times linearly dependent. The rank R is called the *rank of the system*. Thus, the sum of the rank of the system and the degree of reduction is equal to the number of equations.

These ideas will be extremely useful when we have to answer the following question: how many degrees of freedom are *lost* by the system of variables $(x_1 ... x_n)$ if these variables are restrained by having to satisfy certain linear equations? We cannot say, without further examination, that m (linear) equations eliminate m degrees of freedom. For this assertion to be justified it has to be qualified by the following:

First, the equations must not be contradictory. In other words, the rank R of the matrix of (9.17) – i.e. the rank of (8.36) – must be the same as the rank r of (8.35).

Secondly, the number of the degrees of freedom of $(x_1 ... x_n)$ is diminished not by m, but by $(m-P)$, i.e. by R, which is by definition the rank of the system of equations. Thus the assertion that the number of

94

degrees of freedom is diminished by m is exact only in the case when the rank of the m equations is as high as it possibly can be (when the number of the equations is equal to or less than the number of unknowns). Thus the number of the degrees of freedom is

$$(9.22) \qquad n - R \quad \text{i.e.} \quad (n - m) + P.$$

It is sufficient to refer to (8.37) to ascertain that this is in fact so. If $r = R$ (which is indispensable, in virtue of (8.34), for the equations to be noncontradictory), the number of the degrees of freedom of the solution $(x_1 \ldots x_n)$ is in fact equal to $n - r$, in other words to $n - R$, which, by the definition (9.21), is equal to $(n - m) + P$.

(9.22) can be also expressed by saying that if the n variables $(x_1 \ldots x_n)$ are restrained by having to satisfy m equations, these variables lose m degrees of freedom, but at the same time they acquire P degrees of freedom if the linear equations in question are P times linearly dependent.

SUPPLEMENT

Let us consider n sectors of the economy (which can be represented graphically by points of a plane), and the flows which can circulate in all directions from one sector to another. If we assume that there is no flow leaving a sector and returning to it directly (without passing through other sectors) ("loops"), there are (in principle) $\binom{n}{2} = n(n - 1)/2$ different flows to consider; however, certain flows can be assumed to be zero in a given problem.

First, we are going to consider a closed system in complete equilibrium; this means that there is no connection between the system of n sectors and the rest of the world, and that moreover each sector is in equilibrium: the total amount sent out is equal to the total amount received. We wish to determine the number of degrees of freedom of such a system. This problem depends in fact on the theory of finite graphs, and its solution can be expounded very simply.

Let x_{kh} be the net value of the flow going from sector k to sector h (which can be positive, negative, or zero). The $\binom{n}{2}$ flows x_{kh} (for $k = 1, 2, \ldots, n - 1$; $h = k + 1$, $k + 2, \ldots, n$) are sufficient to describe the system, and in general, if all our conditions are satisfied, a much smaller number will be sufficient. For obvious typographical reasons, we will also consider the flows x_{hk} for $k \leqslant h$, which are defined by

$$(2) \qquad x_{hk} = - x_{kh} \qquad (k = 1, 2, \ldots, n; h = 1, 2, \ldots, n)$$

From (2), we deduce

$$(3) \qquad x_{hh} = 0 ,$$

which conforms to the hypothesis which we have made above. The fact that each sector taken in isolation must be in equilibrium is expressed by

$$(4) \qquad \sum_{h=1}^{n} x_{kh} = 0 \qquad (k = 1, 2, ..., n)$$

Because of (2), only $(n - 1)$ of the equations of (4) are linearly independent; this will be seen from the following line of reasoning, and from the examples.

At first, we suppose that none of the flows is put equal to zero; to find now the exact number of the degrees of freedom, we consider point No. 1. There are $(n - 1)$ flows meeting at this point. If we give arbitrary values to $(n - 2)$ of these flows, the value of the last one can be calculated from equation (4) (with $k = 1$). Next, we consider point No. 2; one of the flows meeting there (x_{12}) is already determined; as for the remaining ones, we give arbitrary values to $(n - 3)$ of them, while the value of the last one is calculated from equation (4). When we come to point No. 3, the values x_{13} and x_{23} are already determined, and we can choose $(n - 4)$ of the remaining values arbitrarily, etc.; when we come to point No. $(n - 1)$, we have chosen

$$(5) \qquad (n - 2) + (n - 3) + \cdots + 1 = \binom{n}{2} - n + 1$$

arbitrary values. When we come to the last point, all the flows will have been determined.

If $v \geqslant 1$ of the $\binom{n}{2}$ flows are put equal to zero, this imposes v independent constraints (apart from the case of degeneracy), and in (5) we must replace $\binom{n}{2}$ by $N = \binom{n}{2} - v$, N being now the number of flows actually circulating. To sum up,

$$(6) \qquad \left. \begin{array}{l} \text{The number of degrees of} \\ \text{freedom in a closed system} \\ \text{in complete equilibrium,} \\ \text{composed of } n \text{ sectors} \\ \text{connected by } N \text{ flows.} \end{array} \right\} = N - n + 1$$

Let us now suppose that each of the n sectors is also connected with the rest of the world by a net contribution $A_k (k = 1, 2, ..., n)$, the system of n sectors still being in equilibrium with the rest of the world, that is

$$(7) \qquad \sum_{k=1}^{n} A_k = 0 .$$

As previously, each sector is assumed to be in equilibrium, but the equation of equilibrium now takes the form

$$(8) \qquad \sum_{h=1}^{n} x_{kh} + A_h = 0 . \qquad (k = 1, 2, ..., n)$$

96

This case reduces easily to the preceding one by considering the rest of the world as a new sector. If no external flows are put equal to zero, the number of the degrees of freedom is now

(9) $\quad \binom{n+1}{2} - v - (n+1) + 1 = \binom{1+n}{2} - \binom{n}{2} + N - n =$

$$= \frac{(n+1)n - n(n-1) - 2n}{2} + N = N$$

N being as before the number of flows actually circulating inside the system of n sectors.

If μ of the exchange-flows with the outside are put equal to zero, let $M = n - \mu$; in the equation (6), N must be replaced not by $N + n$ (which one would do to obtain (9)), but by $N + M$, and n must be replaced as before by $(n + 1)$, which finally leads to

(10) $\quad \left.\begin{array}{l} \text{Number of degrees of freedom} \\ \text{in a system of } n \text{ sectors in} \\ \text{complete equilibrium, with } N \\ \text{internal and } M \text{ external flows} \end{array}\right\} = N + M - n$

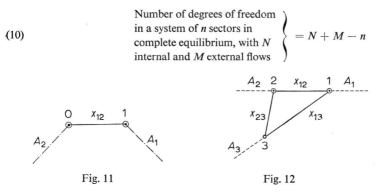

Fig. 11   Fig. 12

Figures 11 and 12 illustrate the cases $n = 2$ and $n = 3$; if $n = 2$, and there are no external flows, one has obviously $x_{12} = 0$, thus there is no degree of freedom; this confirms (5), which gives $1 - 2 + 1 = 0$. If there are two external flows A_1 and A_2, they must be equal in absolute value and opposite in sign, and x_{12} must be equal to $- A_1$. Thus, there is one degree of freedom; this is confirmed by (9), with $N = \binom{n}{2}$ and $n = 2$.

In figure 12, one has

$$x_{12} + x_{13} + A_1 = 0$$
$$x_{23} - x_{12} + A_2 = 0$$
$$- x_{13} - x_{23} + A_3 = 0$$

If A_1 and x_{13} are given, one deduces x_{12} from the first equation. If A_2 is also given, one deduces x_{23} from the second equation. In virtue of (7), the last equation is the sum of the first two. The number of arbitrarily chosen parameters is 3 here, which is confirmed by (9), with $N = \binom{n}{2} = 3$.

If one of the three external flows is put equal to zero, we will lose one degree of freedom, which is confirmed by (10) with $N = \binom{n}{2} = 3$, $M = 2$, $n = 3$. If two external flows are put equal to zero, the third one will be zero automatically because of (7);

the system of three sectors will be closed. It is intuitively clear that in this case the same flow would circulate from point No. 1 to point No. 2, and from there to point No. 3, and back to No. 1, giving one degree of freedom, which is confirmed by (5):

$$\binom{3}{2} - 3 + 1 = 1$$

One could also use (10), on the condition, however, that we remember that the number of external flows which are put equal to zero is only $\mu = 2$, so that one has $M = 1$, whence $N = \binom{3}{2}$, $M = 1$, $n = 3$, which gives $3 + 1 - 3 = 1$ degree of freedom.

An analogous line of argument can be applied to the case $n = 2$ if one of the external flows is put equal to zero; in this case (5) gives: $\binom{2}{2} - 2 + 1 = 0$, and (10) gives: $\binom{2}{2} + 1 - 2 = 0$.

In a concrete case, one must in general consider sectors not in equilibrium with each other or with the rest of the world.

Besides, sometimes it is necessary to separate the flow between two sectors into two distinct flows, one going from k to h, the other going from h to k. These more complicated cases are discussed in many reports from the Institute of Economics at the University of Oslo.

EXAMPLES

First, we are going to give a simple example derived from (8.1′) to accustom the reader to the treatment of these problems, and then we will take up example (8.1′)3 again to show the application of the relations of linear dependence through a concrete but less immediate example.

Example (9.1′).

Let us consider the very simple sector of the economy from the beginning of example (8.1′). But this time we imagine that the quantities of inputs which are necessary for the production of goods for final deliveries for the consumers are bought and sold at a fixed market price, which is p for a, and q for b. The man-power receives a universal wage s. We will now ask the question: Given the quantities a_0 and b_0 bought at the beginning, what is the profit β realized?

If λ and μ are the outputs from the production process during the period considered, we have seen that the inputs must be:

$$a_0 = 0.2\,\lambda + 0.7\,\mu$$
$$b_0 = 0.7\,\lambda + 0.1\,\mu$$
$$u = 5\,(\lambda + \mu).$$

The profit must accordingly be

$$\beta = p\lambda + q\mu - pa_0 - qb_0 - su.$$

or after insertion for a_0, b_0 and u:

$$\beta = p\,(0.8\lambda - 0.7\mu) + q\,(-0.7\lambda + 0.9\mu) - 5s\,(\lambda + \mu)$$

98

After rearranging this last equation a bit, we can sum up the problem in this system of equations:

[9.1'] (1) $\begin{cases} \beta = \lambda [0.8p - 0.7q - 5s] + \mu [0.9q - 0.7p - 5s] \\ a_0 = 0.2\lambda \qquad\qquad\qquad\qquad + 0.7\mu \\ b_0 = 0.7\lambda \qquad\qquad\qquad\qquad + 0.1\mu. \end{cases}$

To find in the system [9.1'] (1) the homogeneous linear relation which exists between the three equations, we apply the conditions (9.19). If one must have

$$x\beta + ya_0 + zb_0 \equiv 0,$$

this requires as a necessary and sufficient condition that

$$\begin{cases} x\lambda [0.8p - 0.7q - 5s] + 0.2\lambda y + 0.7\, \lambda z = 0 \\ x\mu [0.9q - 0.7p - 5s] + 0.7\mu y + 0.1\, \mu z = 0, \end{cases}$$

or after dividing through by λ and μ which are not zero

$$x [0.8p - 0.7q - 5s] + 0.2y + 0.7z = 0$$
$$x [0.9q - 0.7p - 5s] + 0.7y + 0.1z = 0,$$

x, y, z must not all be zero simultaneously. More precisely, for the problem to have any interest, x must not be zero here. Let us see now if this can be done by giving to x the value 1, and then trying to calculate y and z. Under these conditions the system can be written as

$$0.2y + 0.7z = 0.7q + 5s - 0.8p$$
$$0.7y + 0.1z = 0.7p + 5s - 0.9q$$

The determinant is

$$\begin{vmatrix} 0.2 & 0.7 \\ 0.7 & 0.1 \end{vmatrix} = -0.47 \neq 0.$$

There exists thus a solution for $x = 1$ which is (the reader should verify)

$$y = \frac{57p + 300s - 70q}{47}$$

$$z = \frac{67q + 250s - 70p}{47}.$$

Hence the relation

$$0 \equiv \beta + \frac{57p + 300s - 70q}{47} a_0 + \frac{67q + 250s - 70p}{47} b_0$$

or

$$\beta \equiv \frac{70q - 57p - 300s}{47} a_0 + \frac{70p - 67q - 250s}{47} b_0$$

EXAMPLE (9.2′).

Let us reconsider example (8.1′)3 with the help of the theory of Chapter IX. The system S_3 can be considered as composed, first, of the system S_3' of the first three and the last two equations in λ_1, λ_2, λ_3, μ_1 and μ_2. It is also easy to see that S_3' has one and only one solution. Thus, the system S_3 admits a solution only if the two intermediate equations on the availability of the products for consumption are consequences of the system S_3'. In this way we obtain the conclusions of the reasoning employed in the study of example (8.1′)3, to which it suffices to refer. The advantage of the approach of Chapter IX over that of Chapter VIII is that the relations of dependence between the equations considered often have a direct origin, which can easily be made evident, and which can be algebraically made explicit with precision.

SECOND ORDER CONDITION AND SUFFICIENT CRITERION FOR LOCAL EXTREMUM IN THE CASE OF TWO VARIABLES WITHOUT CONSTRAINTS

Up to now we have only considered necessary conditions for the extremum of functions of two or more variables. We will now examine if it is possible to formulate also sufficient conditions for the extremum of the same functions. We shall start with functions of two variables.

The quadratic form, the dominant part in the neighbourhood of an extremum, for a function of two variables

First, let us employ the last formula of (5.3) which gives a necessary condition for the first derivative to be zero at the extremum. This asserts that

(10.1) $$f(x_1, x_2) - f(x_1^0, x_2^0) = \frac{r^2}{2}(Q(p_1, p_2) + \Delta)$$

where

(10.2) $$Q(p_1, p_2) = A_{11}p_1^2 + 2A_{12}p_1p_2 + A_{22}p_2^2.$$

(10.3) $$A_{ij} = f_{ij}^0$$

(10.4) $$\Delta = \frac{r}{3}[f_{111}^\theta p_1^3 + 3f_{112}^\theta p_1^2 p_2 + 3f_{122}^\theta p_1 p_2^2 + f_{222}^\theta p_2^3].$$

The values p_1, p_2 are the coordinates of a point on the unit circle, i.e. they satisfy (5.12) and r satisfies (5.13). The values A_{ij} have been introduced solely to avoid using the index 0. These coefficients are constants, when the p vary.

Let M_R be a fixed upper bound for the absolute values of the third derivatives when the point is situated in the neighbourhood defined by R. Then the absolute value of Δ will have the upper bound given by

(10.5) $$|\Delta| \leqslant \frac{R}{3}M_R(|p_1| + |p_2|)^3.$$

In the case of two variables, the quadratic form can be positive definite, negative definite, indefinite, and semidefinite

By taking R sufficiently small, we can achieve that the value of Δ on the right hand side of (10.1) should be less than an arbitrary number given in advance. In this way the sign of the whole right hand side of (10.1) will depend on the sign of the values which the quadratic form appearing on the right hand side of (10.1) is capable of taking. The resulting situation can be classified into the following four cases:

I. The quadratic form Q is positive definite, or more precisely, positive definite and non-singular. In this case, the coefficients A_{ij} are such that the value of Q remains always strictly positive, provided the variables satisfy (5.12). In other words, whatever choice we make for the numbers p_1 and p_2 – provided that we take care to satisfy (5.12) – the value of Q will remain greater than or equal to a certain strictly positive number. For an example, we can take $Q = A_{11}p_1^2 + A_{22}p_2^2$, where A_{11} and A_{12} are both strictly positive. Since the term Δ can be taken as small as we wish by reducing the radius R of the neighbourhood considered, it is clear that we can define in this way a neighbourhood in which the whole expression (10.1) is everywhere strictly positive. In the present case, we can thus be certain that the point (x_1^0, x_2^0) is a minimum for the function f.

II. The quadratic form is negative definite, or more precisely, negative definite and non-singular. In this case the coefficients A_{ij} are such that, whatever the values of p_1 and p_2 (provided that they satisfy (5.12)), the value of Q remains strictly negative. One such example is $Q = A_{11}p_1^2 + A_{22}p_2^2$, where A_{11} and A_{22} are both strictly negative. A line of reasoning analogous to the one which we have given in case (I) shows that the point (x_1^0, x_2^0) is necessarily a maximum for the function f.

III. The quadratic form is indefinite. In this case there exist values p_1 and p_2 which make the expression strictly positive, and others which make it strictly negative. We can give, as an example, $Q = A_{11}p_1^2 + A_{22}p_2^2$, where one of the coefficients A_{11} and A_{22} is strictly positive and the other is strictly negative. Within the limits of the neighbourhood considered, there will be points where the value of the function f is greater, and other points where it is less than the value of f at the initial point (x_1^0, x_2^0). Clearly in this case we can be sure that (x_1^0, x_2^0) is neither a maximum, nor a minimum. Since Q is a continuous function of p_1 and p_2, we can also conclude that there will be necessarily one or more pairs (p_1, p_2), such that $Q=0$. For these pairs of values the sign of the right hand side of (10.1) is not determined by the sign of the quadratic form. Thus, it happens occasionally that the term Δ itself is decisive. This is without consequence, since values of the quadratic form at other points provides us with the desired information that the point (x_1^0, x_2^0) cannot be an extremum.

IV. The quadratic form is semi-definite, that is, there exist values p_1 and p_2 satisfying (5.12) and such that the quadratic form Q vanishes for these values, and is always of the same sign for all other values of p_1 and p_2. We can say that in this case the quadratic form Q does not "pass through" zero, but only "touches" it. As an example we give $Q=A_{11}p_1^2+A_{22}p_2^2$, where one of the coefficients A_{11} and A_{22} is exactly equal to zero, while the other is different from zero. In this case the structure of the quadratic form is not sufficient to decide if there is an extremum here. In fact, if the quadratic form vanishes for a pair of values p_1, p_2, in any small neighbourhood of (p_1, p_2) the sign of the whole right hand side of (10.1) is determined by the sign of Δ and we need further information. The sign of Δ at the afore-mentioned point is not unimportant any more, as it was in case (III), since this time, by definition, Q retains the same sign for all the other values of p_1 and p_2. Thus, if at the points where Q is zero, Δ has the same sign that Q has for the other values of p_1 and p_2, we shall have an extremum in the strong sense; while if the sign of Δ is the opposite of Q, there is no extremum. Finally, in the case when Δ is zero at the points in question, we shall have an extremum in the weak sense, that is, in the vicinity of (x_1^0, x_2^0) there are points where the function f has the same value as at the point (x_1^0, x_2^0) itself, but there are no points where it would take greater (respectively smaller) values than at (x_1^0, x_2^0). To sum up, we see that in case (IV) we cannot formulate a distinct answer without an appeal to the derivatives of the third order, or even higher order. We shall not examine this special case here.

These four cases correspond to the cases considered in the discussion of the extrema of a function of one variable

If we now compare the four afore-mentioned cases with the situations which can arise when the function f depends on a single variable only, we find the following analogies:

(I) corresponds to the case in which the second derivative of a function of one variable is positive at the point in question.

(II) corresponds to the case in which the second derivative of a function of one variable is negative at the point in question.

(III) cannot exist for a function of one variable. In fact, the quadratic form consists then of one square term multiplied by a coefficient. Whatever this coefficient, it is impossible that the square terms should be positive for certain values and negative for others. Thus at least two variables are needed to produce case (III).

(IV) corresponds to the case in which the second derivative of a function of one variable is zero, and in which we have to refer to a higher derivative to decide whether the point in question is an extremum, and if so, of what type.

Preliminaries to the study of quadratic forms

The question which now arises is whether we can formulate simple and clear criteria – derived from the structure of the coefficients A_{ij} – corresponding to the afore-mentioned four cases (I)–(IV). To get our bearings, we will study at first the character of the quadratic form

$$(10.6) \qquad Q = Q(\xi_1, \xi_2) = A_{11}\xi_1^2 + 2A_{12}\xi_1\xi_2 + A_{22}\xi_2^2$$

from a completely general point of view and, for the time being we will abstain from imposing special conditions of the form

$$(10.7) \qquad \qquad \xi_1^2 + \xi_2^2 = 1.$$

Having introduced the quadratic form in these general terms, we can later introduce a condition of type (10.7) which is equivalent to considering the variation of Q specially along the unit circle, in other words to observing the condition expressed earlier by (5.12).

We can represent the quadratic form (10.6) graphically by means of a surface touching the plane (ξ_1, ξ_2), as shown by figure (10.8), where the surface Q is situated completely on one side of the plane (ξ_1, ξ_2), and has the appearance of an eggshell whose tip lies at the origin of the plane. This is one of the cases which can arise.

104

Let us suppose that we divide the surface Q by a plane passing through the origin of the plane (ξ_1, ξ_2), and perpendicular to that plane. We obtain the curve of intersection ABC. If we consider this curve itself as a curve drawn in the plane, we see that it is symmetrical. It is simply a curve representing a function of the form cr^2, where r is the abscissa

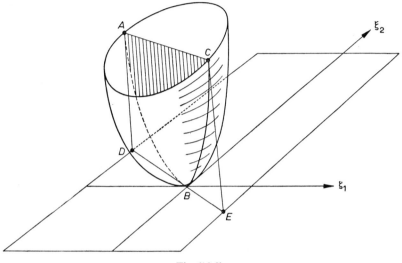

Fig. (10.8)

calculated with respect to a horizontal axis in the intersecting plane, that is, the axis DBE with its origin at B. From the point of view of the plane (ξ_1, ξ_2), this axis DBE is defined by the radius vector of the projection onto the plane (ξ_1, ξ_2) of the point describing the curve of intersection. The symmetry of the curve of intersection results immediately from the fact that we can write the quadratic form as

(10.9) $\qquad Q = cr^2 \quad$ in which $\quad c = A_{11}p_1^2 + 2A_{12}p_1p_2 + A_{22}p_2^2.$

If p_1 and p_2 are given, the radius vector passing through the origin is determined, and if the direction of DBE is thus determined, the value c in (10.9) is a constant. Thus, each choice of p_1 and p_2 will give a curve of intersection of the form cr^2, c being a constant; but it is not certain that this constant is positive in every case, as it is in Figure (10.8). This is now precisely the question. According to the position of the intersecting plane, i.e. according to the direction of the line DBE in the plane (ξ_1, ξ_2), the constant c will take different values. Will it remain always strictly positive, whatever the orientation of DBE? Or will it remain strictly negative? Or, again, will it be positive for certain directions of this line, and negative for other directions, in which case, by continuity, it will vanish for certain positions? Or, finally, will the constant c preserve its sign, but nevertheless vanish for certain positions of the plane, i.e. for certain values of p_1 and p_2? These four possibilities reproduce the four cases (I)–(IV) which we have considered above.

Variations of the value Q when the argument varies along the unit circle

In order to state the exact criteria concerning the proper circumstances which give rise to the four possibilities, we are going to follow the variation of the value Q when the argument lies on the unit-circle of the plane (ξ_1, ξ_2). In other words, we now consider Q as a function of the two variables p_1 and p_2 satisfying (5.12). This amounts to imagining that we interesect the surface Q with a cylinder, which is perpendicular to the plane (ξ_1, ξ_2), and whose base is a circle of radius 1. The resulting situation is illustrated by figure (10.10), in which the circle of radius 1 is indicated by $ABCD$. The curve of intersection of the surface Q with the cylinder is represented by $A'B'C'D'$. This curve of intersection gives us all the information we need about Q.

In fact, the value of the ordinate along this curve, i.e. the distance of the point from the (ξ_1, ξ_2) plane is the same as the value of c in (10.9). Thus, if the value of the ordinate of the said point remains always strictly positive as it describes the curve – as in the case illustrated by figure (10.10) – we have the first of the aforementioned cases (I)–(IV). If, on the contrary, the value of the ordinate remains strictly negative from the beginning to the end, we are dealing with case (II). If the curve of intersection has sometimes a strictly positive ordinate (i.e. when it is situated above the plane (ξ_1, ξ_2), and sometimes a strictly negative ordinate (i.e. when it is situated below that plane) – as illustrated by figure (10.11) – we are dealing with case (III). Finally, if the curve $A'B'C'D'$ remains always on one side of the plane, but curves downwards and touches the plane (ξ_1, ξ_2) at two points of a line passing through the origin – see figure (10.12) – we have case (IV).

106

To know with which case we are dealing in a given problem, we look for the greatest and the smallest value taken by Q as the point representing the argument of Q moves once around the unit circle. In this way we are led to study a new maximum and minimum problem. Its solution will help us to decide whether or not the original extremum problem concerning the function f has itself a solution. This new problem is simpler than the preceding one. In fact, the only information concerning the function f

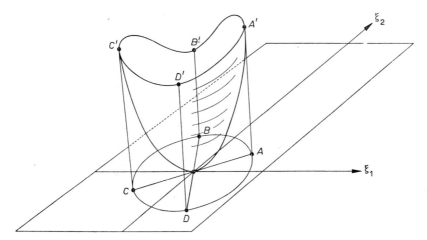

Fig. (10.10)

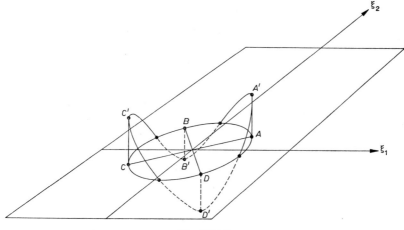

Fig. (10.11)

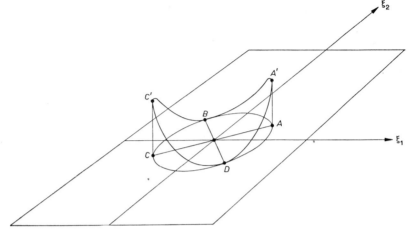

Fig. (10.12)

was that it had three continuous (and moreover bounded) derivatives, while we are now considering a well determined type of function, namely, a quadratic form. This will permit us to solve the new maximum and minimum problem in a precise and elegant manner.

We have to study the extrema of the quadratic form $Q(p_1, p_2)$ under the condition (5.12). We consider now the curve of intersection $A'B'C'D'$ in figures (10.10) to (10.12). If it appears that the smallest value of the form $Q(p_1, p_2)$ is strictly positive, we have obviously case (I), and if it is confirmed that the greatest value of $Q(p_1, p_2)$ is strictly negative, we have case (II). On the other hand, if the greatest value of $Q(p_1, p_2)$ is positive, but its smallest value is negative, we have case (III). That is essentially what we want to know. However, if it appears in the sequel that it is possible to formulate valid criteria concerning case (IV) too, we will not fail to do so.

The necessary first-order conditions for the extrema of a quadratic form

We have thus stated the problem in a simple and elegant form: Since $Q(p_1, p_2)$ is a continuous function of the variables p_1 and p_2, with continuous partial derivatives of all order, and since the point (p_1, p_2) varies continuously, without endpoints, along the unit circle, it follows that $Q(p_1, p_2)$ will take those values – and only those values – which are

108

contained between its greatest and smallest local extremum. Now, the argument employed in Chapter VI permits us to formulate a necessary condition for these extrema; in other words, we can find a set of points which will include all the local extrema of Q. Once we have determined these points (and it turns out that there is a finite number of them), we only have to calculate the value of $Q(p_1, p_2)$ at each of these points. We can be sure, – the conditions for the variation of p_1 and p_2 being given – that Q will take those values, and only those values, which are situated in the continuous interval contained between the maximal and minimal values of Q calculated above. We are justified in drawing this conclusion without examining whether each one of these points is or is not an extremum. This conclusion concerning the values taken by Q as the point (p_1, p_2) makes one complete circuit of the unit circle, follows from the fact that we can be certain that there is no local extremum of $Q(p_1, p_2)$ which does not belong to the set of points which we have determined by referring to the necessary conditions for the extrema of $Q(p_1, p_2)$.

The characteristic equation in the case of two variables

The necessary condition for the local extremum of $Q(p_1, p_2)$ – which we have just noted – is derived directly from the results of Chapter VI. We simply form the function

(10.13) $$\Phi(p_1, p_2) = Q(p_1, p_2) - \lambda(p_1^2 + p_2^2)$$

and formulate the necessary first order condition for the extremum of Φ. (The use of $(-\lambda)$ as a multiplier instead of λ is obviously only a typographical change). Thus we obtain the condition

(10.14) $$\begin{aligned}(A_{11} - \lambda)p_1 + A_{12}p_2 &= 0, \\ A_{21}p_1 + (A_{22} - \lambda)p_2 &= 0.\end{aligned}$$

(For reasons of symmetry we have written A_{21} instead of A_{12} in the second equation of (10.14); we have the right to do this since the numbers A_{ij} are symmetrical and consequently $A_{ij}=A_{ji}$.)

For the point p_1, p_2 to give a local extremum of the quadratic form $Q(p_1, p_2)$ under the condition (5.12), it is thus necessary that there exist a number λ statisfying (10.14). We can say in fact more about this number: it is equal to the value of Q at the point (p_1, p_2) under consideration. This assertion is easily verified by multiplying the first equation of (10.14) by p_1 and the second by p_2, and adding the products together. In view of of (5.12) we obtain

(10.15) $$\lambda = A_{11}p_1^2 + 2A_{12}p_1p_2 + A_{22}p_2^2.$$

In fact, we can say more about this number λ. According to the theory of homogeneous linear equations, we know that a system of equations like (10.14) cannot have a solution like (p_1, p_2) (i.e. a solution not identically zero) unless the determinant of the coefficients on the left hand side is zero. Consequently we must have

(10.16) $$\begin{vmatrix} A_{11} - \lambda & A_{12} \\ A_{21} & A_{22} - \lambda \end{vmatrix} = 0.$$

and thus, if there exists a local extremum for the quadratic form $Q(p_1, p_2)$ under the condition (5.12), there exists necessarily a number λ, which on one hand is equal to the value of the quadratic form $Q(p_1, p_2)$ at the point of extremum, and on the other hand satisfies (10.16). Now this is the same as saying that every local extremum of the quadratic form $Q(p_1, p_2)$ must satisfy (10.16). In other words, the values taken by $Q(p_1, p_2)$ as the unit circle is described once must be contained between the greatest and smallest number λ satisfying (10.16).

The characteristic roots and the complete classification of all possibilities in the case of two variables

The reverse is also true: every number λ satisfying (10.16) is necessarily a value which the quadratic form $Q(p_1, p_2)$ is capable of taking as the unit circle is described once. In fact, let us suppose that λ is a number satisfying (10.16). The theory of linear equations teaches us that the system (10.14) always has at least one solution (p_1, p_2) where the two numbers p_1 and p_2 are not both zero (cf. (8.31)). This solution is determined but for an arbitrary factor, i.e. if the values of p_1 and p_2 of the solution are multiplied by an arbitrary factor (the same for p_1 and p_2), a new solution is obtained because of the homogeneity of the equations (10.14). We can thus always find a solution p_1, p_2 satisfying (5.12). Substituting these numbers into (10.14), one establishes between λ and p_1, p_2 the same relation as in (10.15). That is to say that the λ in question

110

is necessarily a value effectively taken by the quadratic form $Q(p_1, p_2)$ as the unit circle is described once.

This reasoning proves first of all the following theorem.

THEOREM (10.17). Every root of the characteristic equation (10.16) is real if the coefficients A_{ij} are real and symmetrical, i.e. if $A_{ij} = A_{ji}$.

In the second place, it proves the following fundamental theorem about the quadratic form $Q(p_1, p_2)$:

THEOREM (10.18). When (p_1, p_2) describes a complete circuit on the unit circle (5.12), the quadratic form $Q(p_1, p_2)$ takes those values, and only those values, which are contained between two roots of the characteristic equation (10.16), the values of the two roots being included.

In this way we have stated a convenient and elegant criterion concerning the four case (I)–(IV) formulated above. This criterion can also be formulated in the following way.

Since the characteristic equation (10.16) has only real roots, we determine the greater and the smaller root. If the smaller of these roots is strictly positive, we have case (I). If the greater root is strictly negative, we have case (II). If the greater is strictly positive, and the smaller is strictly negative we have case (III). Finally, if one of the two is exactly zero, we have case (IV). There are no other possibilities.

Here the characteristic equation is of the second degree, and its roots are

$$(10.19) \quad \lambda = \frac{A_{11} + A_{22}}{2} \pm \sqrt{\left(\frac{A_{11} + A_{22}}{2}\right)^2 - (A_{11}A_{22} - A_{12}^2)}.$$

Thus we are now in the position to verify immediately that the two roots are real in conformity with our conclusions above. In fact, the term under the square root can be written in the form

$$\left(\frac{A_{11} - A_{22}}{2}\right)^2 + A_{12}^2.$$

(10.19) now permits us to formulate in terms of the coefficients A_{ij} the criteria for the four cases (I)–(IV). We have

(I)   if $A_{11}A_{22} - A_{12}^2 > 0$ and $A_{11} > 0$

(or, which is the same, if $A_{22} > 0$)

111

(II)   if $A_{11}A_{22} - A_{12}^2 > 0$ and $A_{11} < 0$

(or, which is the same, if $A_{22} < 0$)

(10.20)

(III)   if $A_{11}A_{22} - A_{12}^2 < 0$

(IV) $A_{11}A_{22} - A_{12}^2 = 0$

If our purpose had been to obtain with the least effort a result which is applicable to the case of two variables, we could have proceeded at once to the discussion of the criteria (10.20). We could have accomplished our task quicker this way than by means of the analysis which we have given above, but then we would not have been able to lay clearly the foundation of a generalisation applicable to functions of n variables. The great advantage of the form of exposition which we have chosen is that it opens up a clear road to this generalisation.

SUPPLEMENT

To verify directly that $A_{11}p_1^2 + 2A_{12}p_1p_2 + A_{22}p_2^2$ remains always between $\lambda_1(p_1^2 + p_2^2)$ and $\lambda_2(p_1^2 + p_2^2)$, where λ_1 and λ_2 are the roots of the equation (10.16). This is a verification of the remarks made in the middle of page 110.

First, it is easily verified that the discriminant of the equation (10.16) is

$$(A_{11} - A_{22})^2 + 4A_{12}^2 \geqslant 0$$

and that the equation can be written as:

(a)
$$\frac{A_{11} - \lambda}{A_{12}} = \frac{A_{12}}{A_{22} - \lambda}.$$

Now, to compare

$$A_{11}p_1^2 + 2A_{12}p_1p_2 + A_{22}p_2^2$$

with $\lambda_1 (p_1^2 + p_2^2)$, we simply take the difference

$$\Delta_1 = A_{11}p_1^2 + 2A_{12}p_1p_2 + A_{22}p_2^2 - \lambda_1 (p_1^2 + p_2^2)$$

and after rearrangement, this gives

$$\Delta_1 = (A_{11} - \lambda_1) p_1^2 + 2A_{12}p_1p_2 + (A_{22} - \lambda_1) p_2^2.$$

We now take (a) into account, replacing for example $A_{11} - \lambda$ by its expression derived from (a), which leads to

$$\Delta_1 = \frac{A_{12}^2}{A_{22} - \lambda_1} p_1^2 + 2A_{12}p_1p_2 + (A_{22} - \lambda_1) p_2^2.$$

112

Simple factorisation is sufficient to produce a perfect square:

$$\Delta_1 = \frac{1}{A_{22} - \lambda_1} \left[A_{12}p_1 + (A_{22} - \lambda_1) p_2\right]^2.$$

Since the smaller root is equal to:

$$\lambda_1 = A_{22} + \frac{A_{11} - A_{22}}{2} - \sqrt{\left(\frac{A_{11} - A_{22}}{2}\right)^2 + A_{12}^2}$$

it is seen that $A_{22} - \lambda_1 > 0$ if $A_{12} \neq 0$, and consequently $\Delta_1 \geqslant 0$.

EXAMPLES

EXAMPLE (10.1′).

Find and discuss the extrema of the function of two variables

$$f(x_1, x_2) = \frac{x_1 + x_2}{3 + x_1^2 + x_2^2 + x_1x_2}.$$

First, we look for the points which satisfy the local necessary conditions of the first order, according to Chapter V. We obtain the system S:

$$S \begin{cases} f'_{x_1} = \dfrac{1}{3 + x_1^2 + x_2^2 + x_1x_2} - \dfrac{(2x_1 + x_2)(x_1 + x_2)}{(3 + x_1^2 + x_2^2 + x_1x_2)^2} = 0 \\[3mm] f'_{x_2} = \dfrac{1}{3 + x_1^2 + x_2^2 + x_1x_2} - \dfrac{(x_1 + 2x_2)(x_1 + x_2)}{(3 + x_1^2 + x_2^2 + x_1x_2)^2} = 0. \end{cases}$$

By subtraction, S gives the necessary condition

$$\frac{(x_1 + x_2)(x_2 - x_1)}{(3 + x_1^2 + x_2^2 + x_1x_2)^2} = 0$$

which splits up into

$$x_1 + x_2 = 0$$
$$x_2 - x_1 = 0.$$

The reader will easily verify that the substitution of the first condition $x_1 + x_2 = 0$ into S gives an impossibility. The second condition gives (e.g. by putting $x_1 = x_2 = a$):

$$\frac{1}{3 + 3a^2} - \frac{3a \cdot 2a}{(3 + 3a^2)^2} = 0$$

or

$$3 + 3a^2 - 6a^2 = 0 \qquad \text{or} \qquad 3 = 3a^2;$$

or

$$\begin{cases} a = x_1 = x_2 = +1 \\ a = x_1 = x_2 = -1. \end{cases}$$

For each of these two extrema, the function f and its derivatives of all order are well defined. Let us investigate more closely the nature of these extrema. First we consider the case $x_1 = x_2 = 1$.

Denoting by D the denominator

$$3 + x_1{}^2 + x_2{}^2 + x_1 x_2$$

we can write the second derivatives as:

$$f''_{x_1{}^2} = \frac{-(2x_1 + x_2)}{D^2} - \frac{2(x_1 + x_2) + (2x_1 + x_2)}{D^2} + \frac{2(2x_1 + x_2)^2(x_1 + x_2)}{D^3}$$

$$f''_{x_1 x_2} = \frac{-(x_1 + 2x_2)}{D^2} - \frac{(x_1 + x_2) + (2x_1 + x_2)}{D^2} + \frac{2(x_1 + 2x_2)(2x_1 + x_2)(x_1 + x_2)}{D^3}$$

$$f''_{x_2{}^2} = \frac{-(x_1 + 2x_2)}{D^2} - \frac{2(x_1 + x_2) + (x_1 + 2x_2)}{D^2} + \frac{2(x_1 + 2x_2)^2(x_1 + x_2)}{D^3}.$$

For $x_1 = x_2 = 1$ the numerical values of these derivatives are

$$f''_{x_1{}^2} = -\frac{3}{36} - \frac{7}{36} + \frac{36}{216} = \frac{-10 + 6}{36} = -\frac{4}{36} = -\frac{1}{9}$$

$$f''_{x_1 x_2} = -\frac{3}{36} - \frac{5}{36} + \frac{36}{216} = \frac{-8 + 6}{36} = -\frac{2}{36}$$

$$f''_{x_2{}^2} = -\frac{3}{36} - \frac{7}{36} + \frac{36}{216} = \frac{-10 + 6}{36} = -\frac{4}{36} = -\frac{1}{9}.$$

Thus

$$f(x_1, x_2) = f(1, 1) + \frac{1}{2}\left[-\frac{1}{9}u^2 - 2\frac{2}{36}uv - \frac{1}{9}v^2\right] + \cdots$$

$$f(x_1, x_2) = f(1, 1) - \frac{1}{18}[u^2 + uv + v^2] + \cdots$$

$$= \frac{1}{3} - \frac{1}{2}\frac{1}{9}[u^2 + uv + v^2] + \cdots$$

In view of the theory we must investigate the non-identically zero solutions of the system obtained by putting the partial derivatives of

$$-\left[\frac{u^2}{9} + \frac{uv}{9} + \frac{v^2}{9}\right] - \lambda(u^2 + v^2)$$

equal to zero. This gives

$$\left.\begin{array}{l} f'_u = -\dfrac{2u}{9} - \dfrac{v}{9} - 2\lambda u = -2u\left[\dfrac{1}{9} + \lambda\right] - \dfrac{v}{9} = 0 \\[4mm] f'_v = -\dfrac{u}{9} - \dfrac{2v}{9} - 2\lambda v = -\dfrac{u}{9} - 2v\left[\dfrac{1}{9} + \lambda\right] = 0 \end{array}\right\} S_1.$$

114

This has non-identically zero solutions in u and v only if S_1 is of rank 1. This gives the condition

$$\begin{vmatrix} -2\left[\dfrac{1}{9} + \lambda\right] & -\dfrac{1}{9} \\[2ex] -\dfrac{1}{9} & -2\left[\dfrac{1}{9} + \lambda\right] \end{vmatrix} = 0$$

or

$$4\left(\frac{1}{9} + \lambda\right)^2 - \left(\frac{1}{9}\right)^2 = 0.$$

or

$$\begin{cases} \dfrac{1}{9} + \lambda = \dfrac{1}{2} \times \dfrac{1}{9} & \lambda = -\dfrac{1}{18} \\[3ex] \dfrac{1}{9} + \lambda = -\dfrac{1}{2} \times \dfrac{1}{9} & \lambda = -\dfrac{3}{18} \end{cases}$$

The two roots λ are both negative. Consequently

$$-\left(\frac{u^2}{9} + \frac{uv}{9} + \frac{v^2}{9}\right)$$

is throughout negative, (its value is in fact between $-1/18$ and $-3/18$, if u and v are restricted by $u^2 + v^2 = 1$) and we have thus found a true maximum, for which, to sum up

$$x_1 = x_2 = 1 \quad \text{and} \quad f(x_1, x_2) = \frac{1}{3}.$$

It remains to consider the case when $x_1 = x_2 = -1$. We leave it to the reader to deal with this question, either by repeating the calculation as an exercise, or by means of the simple remark that $f(x_1, x_2)$ is a function which changes sign if x_1 and x_2 are replaced by $-x_1$ and $-x_2$.

REMARK. We have introduced the auxiliary variable λ to prepare the reader for the case of more than two variables: since this method is the simplest to generalize.

However, in the case of two variables it is often more convenient to study directly the second order part of the increment, i.e.

$$-\frac{1}{2}\left[\frac{u^2}{9} + \frac{uv}{9} + \frac{v^2}{9}\right].$$

Noting that

$$\frac{u^2}{9} + \frac{uv}{9} \quad \text{is the beginning of the square of} \quad \left(\frac{u}{3} + \frac{v}{6}\right)$$

we can write the above expression as

$$-\frac{1}{2}\left[\left(\frac{u}{3} + \frac{v}{6}\right)^2 + \frac{3v^2}{36}\right].$$

It is clear that this is throughout negative, except when $u = v = 0$, where it is zero. Thus we have obtained a strong maximum.

EXAMPLE (10.2′). To study the extreme of $f(x, y) = e^{x^2-y^2} \log (x^2 + y^2)$. This expression defines f and all its derivatives for every x and y, except for $x = y = 0$.

The first-order condition for the extrema can be written as

$$f'_x = 2x \left[e^{x^2-y^2} \log (x^2 + y^2)\right] + \frac{2x\, e^{x^2-y^2}}{x^2 + y^2}$$

$$= 2x\, e^{x^2-y^2} \left[\log (x^2 + y^2) + \frac{1}{x^2 + y^2}\right]$$

$$f'_y = -2y \left[e^{x^2-y^2} \log (x^2 + y^2)\right] + \frac{2y\, e^{x^2-y^2}}{x^2 + y^2}$$

$$= -2y\, e^{x^2-y^2} \left[\log (x^2 + y^2) - \frac{1}{x^2 + y^2}\right].$$

Since $e^{x^2-y^2}$ is never zero, f'_x and f'_y are zero only when, respectively

and

$$\left. \begin{array}{l} x \left[\log (x^2 + y^2) + \dfrac{1}{x^2 + y^2}\right] = 0 \\[4mm] y \left[\log (x^2 + y^2) - \dfrac{1}{x^2 + y^2}\right] = 0 \end{array} \right\} S$$

The discussion of the system S is simplified by a second remark: namely that

$$\log (x^2 + y^2) + \frac{1}{x^2 + y^2}$$

is never zero. In fact, by writing $x^2 + y^2 = 1/r^2$, this reduces to proving that $\log 1/r^2 + r^2$ is never zero, or else that $r^2 - \log r^2$ is never zero, which is deduced from the fact that log is always less than its argument. Therefore

$$\log r^2 < r^2 \quad \text{or} \quad r^2 - \log r^2 > 0$$

(As an exercise the reader could also verify our remark by finding the maximum and minimum of the function $r^2 - \log r^2$).

Under these conditions S reduces to

$$\begin{cases} x = 0 \\[2mm] y \left[\log (x^2 + y^2) - \dfrac{1}{x^2 + y^2}\right] = 0. \end{cases}$$

Thus one must have $x = 0$, and since y and x cannot be zero simultaneously in this

116

case (we would have to adopt a limit-interpretation), we are left with

$$\log y^2 - \frac{1}{y^2} = 0 \quad \text{or} \quad 2 \log y - \frac{1}{y^2} = 0$$

if we assume that $y > 0$ (the case $y < 0$ can be dealt with by symmetry).

Let us examine graphically if the equation $2 \log y - 1/y^2$ admits solutions for $y > 0$. For this purpose, we represent on the same diagram the curves

$$z_1 = 2 \log y \qquad (C_1)$$

and

$$z_2 = \frac{1}{y^2} \qquad (C_2).$$

The equation under discussion has a solution if and only if (C_1) and (C_2) intersect, and the abscissae of the points of intersections will be the roots we are looking for.

Now (C_1) is the graph of a function which steadily increases from $-\infty$ to $+\infty$, and (C_2) is the graph of a function which steadily decreases from $+\infty$ to zero. Thus, they intersect in a single point with abscissa y_0 (cf. figure $(10.1')$), whose approximate

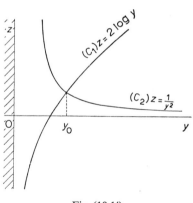

Fig. $(10.1')$

value could, for example, be determined graphically, and found to be greater than 1. Thus, the first order conditions will be satisfied for

$$x = 0 \quad \text{and} \quad y = y_0 \quad \text{defined by} \quad 2 \log y_0 = 1/y_0^2$$

Let us examine this point more closely.

We calculate the second derivatives at this point. We find that

$$f''_{x^2} = 2e^{x^2-y^2}\left[\log(x^2 + y^2) + \frac{1}{x^2 + y^2}\right] + 2x \frac{\partial}{\partial x} \cdots$$

117

$$f''_{xy} = 2x \frac{\partial}{\partial y} \left[e^{x^2 - y^2} \left(\log (x^2 + y^2) + \frac{1}{x^2 + y^2} \right) \right]$$

$$f''_{y^2} = -2 \left[\log (x^2 + y^2) - \frac{1}{x^2 + y^2} \right] \frac{\partial}{\partial y} (y\, e^{x^2 - y^2})$$

$$- 2y\, e^{x^2 - y^2} \left[\frac{2y}{x^2 + y^2} + \frac{2y}{(x^2 + y^2)^2} \right].$$

We have not calculated all the derivatives. In fact, on the one hand we know that all the derivatives exist for $x = 0$, $y = y_0 \neq 0$. On the other hand, we need the values of the derivatives only for $x = 0$, $y = y_0$. Thus we can disregard the terms which contain as a factor x or

$$\log (x^2 + y^2) - \frac{1}{x^2 + y^2}$$

which vanish at the point $x = 0$, $y = y_0$.

Under these conditions the values of the second derivatives are

$$f''_{x^2} = 2e^{-y_0^2} \left[2 \log y_0 + \frac{1}{y_0^2} \right] > 0$$

$$f''_{xy} = 0$$

$$f''_{y^2} = - 2y_0 e^{-y_0^2} \left[\frac{2}{y_0} + \frac{2}{y_0^3} \right] < 0.$$

There is no need to go any further. We have obviously an indefinite form, i.e. case III, and the point $x = 0$, $y = y_0$ is neither a maximum, nor a minimum.

We have an identical situation for $x = 0$, $y = - y_0$.

118

SECOND-ORDER CONDITIONS AND SUFFICIENT CRITERIA FOR THE LOCAL EXTREMUM IN THE CASE OF SEVERAL VARIABLES WITHOUT CONSTRAINTS

Complete formulation of the sufficient conditions in the case of n variables

We consider a function $f(x_1, x_2, \ldots x_n)$ of n variables having continuous third-order partial derivatives in the neighbourhood of a point $(x_1^0, x_2^0, \ldots, x_n^0)$ where

(11.1)
$$\left[\frac{\partial f(x_1, x_2, \ldots, x_n)}{\partial x_i}\right]_{\substack{x_1 = x_1^0 \\ \cdots \\ x_n = x_n^0}} = 0 \qquad (i = 1, 2, \ldots, n).$$

Let

(11.2)
$$A_{ij} = \left[\frac{\partial^2 f(x_1, x_2, \ldots, x_n)}{\partial x_i \partial x_j}\right]_{\substack{x_1 = x_1^0 \\ \cdots \\ x_n = x_n^0}}$$

which implies that $A_{ij} = A_{ji}$.

The characteristic equation

(11.3)
$$\begin{vmatrix} (A_{11} - \lambda) & A_{12} & \ldots & A_{1n} \\ A_{21} & (A_{22} - \lambda) & \ldots & A_{2n} \\ \cdots\cdots\cdots\cdots\cdots\cdots\cdots\cdots\cdots \\ A_{n1} & A_{n2} & \ldots & (A_{nn} - \lambda) \end{vmatrix} = 0$$

has only real roots. Let us determine the greatest root $\lambda_{\max}$ and the smallest root $\lambda_{\min}$ of this equation. (If the number of variables is considerable we can use various methods of approximation which are described in other works.)

The determination of $\lambda_{\max}$ and $\lambda_{\min}$ provides us with the following criteria:

(11.4)

(I) If $\lambda_{\min} > 0$, the point $(x_1^0, x_2^0, \ldots, x_n^0)$ is a local minimum for the function $f(x_1, \ldots, x_n)$. In this case the matrix A_{ij} is positive definite (and non-singular).

(II) If $\lambda_{\max} < 0$, the point $(x_1^0, x_2^0, ..., x_n^0)$ is a local maximum for the function $f(x_1, x_2, ..., x_n)$. In this case the matrix A_{ij} is negative definite (and non-singular).

(III) If $\lambda_{\min} < 0$ and $\lambda_{\max} > 0$, the point $(x_1^0, x_2^0, ..., x_n^0)$ is not an extremum for the function $f(x_1, x_2, ..., x_n)$. In this case the matrix A_{ij} is said to be indefinite.

(IV) If $\lambda_{\max} = 0$ or if $\lambda_{\min} = 0$, the second derivatives at the point $(x_1^0, x_2^0, ..., x_n^0)$, i.e. the matrix A_{ij}, are not sufficient to decide whether or not the point $(x_1^0, x_2^0, ..., x_n^0)$ is also a local extremum for the function $f(x_1, x_2, ..., x_n)$. In this case the matrix A_{ij} is semi-definite.

There are no other possibilities.

We shall not give the proofs of these criteria; these proofs are exact repetitions of those we have given concerning the case $n = 2$ in Chapter X.

The above criteria are obtained when the point representing the argument $(\xi_1, \xi_2, ..., \xi_n)$ of the quadratic form associated with the matrix A_{ij} runs through all the points of the unit sphere of the space $(\xi_1, \xi_2, ..., \xi_n)$ that is

$$(11.5) \qquad \xi_1^2 + \xi_2^2 + \cdots + \xi_n^2 = 1.$$

We could have approached this in a different way, by requiring that instead of $\xi_1^2 + \xi_2^2 + \cdots \xi_n^2$, some other positive definite quadratic form should be equal to 1. However, the criterion given by the formula (11.5) has the advantage of being simple and clear.

Furthermore, we could have formulated the criteria directly by means of the signs of the principal subdeterminants of the matrix A_{ij}, but there is no need to enter into these considerations here.

EXAMPLE

EXAMPLE (11.1').

Let us study the extremum of the function

$$f(x, y, z) = mx^2 e^y + y^2 e^z + z^2 e^x$$

where m is a parameter, at $x = y = z = 0$.

One can easily see that this point satisfies the first-order conditions. We have in fact

$$f'_x = 2mxe^y + z^2 e^x$$
$$f'_y = 2ye^z + mx^2 e^y$$
$$f'_z = 2ze^x + y^2 e^z$$

and these derivatives will truly vanish for $x = y = z = 0$ (whether or not this is the only solution is a much more difficult question, but here we limit ourselves to the neighbourhood of $x = y = z = 0$).

The matrix of the second-order derivatives is as follows:

$$\begin{Vmatrix} 2me^y + z^2e^x & 2mxe^y & 2ze^x \\ 2mxe^y & 2e^z + mx^2e^y & 2ye^z \\ 2ze^x & 2ye^z & 2e^x + y^2e^z \end{Vmatrix}$$

For $x = y = z = 0$, it becomes

$$\begin{Vmatrix} 2m & 0 & 0 \\ 0 & 2 & 0 \\ 0 & & 2 \end{Vmatrix}$$

Thus the characteristic equation will be

$$\begin{vmatrix} (2m - \lambda) & 0 & 0 \\ 0 & (2 - \lambda) & 0 \\ 0 & 0 & (2 - \lambda) \end{vmatrix} \equiv (2 - \lambda)^2 (2m - \lambda) = 0$$

The roots of this equation are 2 and $2m$ (the first is a double root, but this matters very little).

Thus, one can see that if m is positive the two roots are positive and therefore $x = y = z = 0$ is a local minimum for f which takes here the value zero.

If m is negative, one root will be negative and the other positive: there is no extremum.

Finally, if m is zero these criteria are not sufficient to decide the question.

We leave it to the reader to rediscover these results, and even to make them more precise, by considering the sign of $f(x, y, z)$ in the neighbourhood of $x = y = z = 0$.

In particular, it will be seen that if $m = 0$ there is in fact a strong minimum, and that if there exists a minimum for $x = y = z = 0$ it is also a strong minimum.

SECOND-ORDER CONDITIONS AND SUFFICIENT CRITERIA FOR THE LOCAL EXTREMUM IN THE CASE OF SEVERAL VARIABLES WITH CONSTRAINTS

Preparatory discussion of the case of two variables with one constraint

To get our bearings, we shall start by considering the case (6.1)–(6.5), where the problem consisted of determining the maximum of a function $f(x_1, x_2)$ of two variables under a single constraint given by (6.1). The necessary conditions for an extremum of f under this constraint have been formulated in Chapter VI; we now look for sufficient conditions.

Let (x_1^0, x_2^0) be a point satisfying the necessary conditions (6.5). Thus, there exists a number λ such that (6.5) is satisfied at the point (x_1^0, x_2^0). Let us assume that the derivatives C_1 and C_2 are not simultaneously zero at the point (x_1^0, x_2^0).

At first, let us take $C_2 \neq 0$ at (x_1^0, x_2^0). In the neighbourhood of this point, we can consider x_2 as a function of x_1 defined implicitly by (6.1). Let us express this function by $x_2 = \varphi(x_1)$. In the neighbourhood of (x_1^0, x_2^0) we can look upon f as a function of the single variable x_1, that is as the function $f(x_1, \varphi(x_1))$. The derivatives of this function of one variable are

(12.1)
$$\frac{df}{dx_1} = f_1 + f_2 \cdot \varphi',$$

(12.2)
$$\frac{d^2f}{dx_1^2} = (f_{11} + 2f_{12}\varphi' + f_{22}\varphi'^2) + f_2\varphi'',$$

where

(12.3)
$$f_{ij} = \frac{\partial^2 f}{\partial x_i \partial x_j}$$

and

(12.4)
$$\varphi' = \frac{d\varphi(x_1)}{dx_1} \qquad \varphi'' = \frac{d\varphi'(x_1)}{dx_1}.$$

In view of (6.1), we have

(12.5) $$C_1 + C_2\varphi' = 0$$

(in every neighbourhood of (x_1^0, x_2^0))

(12.6) $$(C_{11} + 2C_{12}\varphi' + C_{22}\varphi'^2) + C_2\varphi'' = 0$$

(in every neighbourhood of (x_1^0, x_2^0))

where

(12.7) $$C_{ij} = \frac{\partial^2 C}{\partial x_i \partial x_j}.$$

We assume that f and C have continuous derivatives of all order.
From (12.5) and (12.6), we deduce that

(12.8) $$\varphi' = -\frac{C_1}{C_2}$$

(12.9) $$\varphi'' = -\frac{1}{C_2^3}(C_{11}C_2^2 - 2C_{12}C_1C_2 + C_{22}C_1^2)$$

which, substituted into (12.2), gives at the point (x_1^0, x_2^0)

(12.10) $$\frac{d^2 f}{dx_1^2} = \frac{1}{C_2^2}(A_{11}C_2^2 - 2A_{12}C_1C_2 + A_{22}C_1^2),$$

where

(12.11) $$A_{ij} = f_{ij} + \lambda C_{ij},$$

λ is the number which satisfies (6.5) at (x_1^0, x_2^0). (To be completely precise, we should assign to A, f, and C the index 0, but this would be a useless complication.)

For each point (x_1, x_2) of the neighbourhood of (x_1^0, x_2^0), we can expand $f(x_1, x_2)$ by means of Taylor's formula. Since this expansion is valid generally, it is in particular valid in the case when (x_1, x_2) and (x_1^0, x_2^0) both satisfy (6.1), and when moreover (x_1^0, x_2^0) satisfies the necessary conditions for a conditional local extremum of f. Thus we have

(12.12) $$f(x_1, x_2) - f(x_1^0, x_2^0) = \frac{1}{2}\left[\left(\frac{d^2 f}{dx_1^2}\right)^0 + \Delta\right](x_1 - x_1^0)^2,$$

where Δ can be taken as small as we wish by restricting the neighbourhood of (x_1^0, x_2^0) under consideration. Consequently, if $(d^2f/dx_1^2)^0$ is strictly positive, we are certain that f has a minimum, and if (d^2f/dx_1^2) is strictly

123

negative, we can be sure that it has a maximum. In the present case – the values A_{ij} being given by (12.11) and (6.5) – the right-hand side of (12.10) provides the sufficient criteria straightaway.

The structure of the quadratic form in the case of two variables with one constraint

We shall write the expression of (d^2f/dx_1^2) in such a way that the generalisation to the case of functions of several variables subject to several constraints is intuitively justified.

We replace C_1 and C_2 by p_1 and p_2, according to the transformation

$$(12.13) \qquad C_1 p_1 + C_2 p_2 = 0.$$

(p_1, p_2) being normalised by (5.12). Since we have assumed that $C_2 \neq 0$, p_1 cannot be zero either since p_1 and p_2 cannot both be zero by (5.12). From (12.13), we have

$$(12.14) \qquad C_1 = -\frac{C_2 p_2}{p_1}.$$

Hence, by substitution into (12.10)

$$(12.15) \qquad \frac{d^2 f}{dx_1^2} = \frac{1}{p_1^2}(A_{11}p_1^2 + 2A_{12}p_1 p_2 + A_{22}p_2^2).$$

We should have arrived at a completely similar expression – simply with $1/p_2^2$ before the parenthesis – if we had assumed that $C_1 \neq 0$.

Thus, in the case when at least one of the two partial derivatives C_1 and C_2 is not zero at (x_1^0, x_2^0), the problem of the sufficient criterion can be formulated in the following way: If the two numbers (p_1, p_2) satisfy (12.13) and (5.12), is the quadratic form

$$(12.16) \qquad A_{11}p_1^2 + 2A_{12}p_1 p_2 + A_{22}p_2^2$$

positive or negative?

In this way we have succeeded in stating the problem in a form which is analogous to the form which we have used to study the sufficient conditions in (10.1)–(10.6). Nevertheless, there are two differences. First, the matrix A_{ij} we consider here is not simply the matrix (10.13) of the partial derivatives of f at (x_1^0, x_2^0), but the matrix defined by (12.11). In the

124

second place, the variation of (p_1, p_2) is no longer governed solely by (5.12) but also by (12.13).

The quadratic form in the case of n variables with m constraints

Taking these differences into account, one is intuitively lead to formulate as follows the sufficient criteria in the general case of a function $f(x_1, ..., x_n)$ of n variables, which are restricted by m $(<n)$ constraints of the form (6.9):

We must consider the quadratic form

$$(12.17) \qquad Q(p_1 ... p_n) = \sum_{i=1}^{n} \sum_{j=1}^{n} A_{ij} p_i p_j,$$

where

$$(12.18) \qquad A_{ij} = f_{ij} + \lambda_1 C_{1ij} + \lambda_2 C_{2ij} + \cdots + \lambda_m C_{mij} \qquad \begin{pmatrix} i = 1, 2, ..., n \\ j = 1, 2, ..., n \end{pmatrix}$$

$$(12.19) \qquad C_{hij} = \frac{\partial^2 C_h(x_1 ... x_n)}{\partial x_i \partial x_j} \qquad \begin{pmatrix} h = 1, 2, ..., m \\ i = 1, 2, ..., n \\ j = 1, 2, ..., n \end{pmatrix}$$

and where $\lambda_1, ..., \lambda_m$ are the numbers which are defined by the necessary criterion for the constrained extremum. These numbers can be expressed by means of the values f_i and C_{hi} (cf. (6.17) and (6.10)).

We assume that the variation of $(p_1, ..., p_n)$ is governed by

$$(12.20) \qquad \sum_{i=1}^{n} C_{hi} p_i = 0 \qquad (h = 1, 2, ..., m)$$

$$(12.21) \qquad p_1^2 + \cdots + p_n^2 = 1.$$

It is understood that f_i, C_{hi}, f_{ij}, C_{hij} are the values at the point $(x_1^0, ..., x_n^0)$.

I. If the quadratic form Q defined by (12.17) remains strictly positive under all admissible variation of its argument, f has a local minimum at $(x_1^0, ..., x_n^0)$.

II. If Q remains strictly negative under all such variation of its argument, f has a local maximum at $(x_1^0, ..., x_n^0)$.

III. If Q is strictly positive for at least one admissible value of its argument, and strictly negative for at least one other admissible value, f has neither a minimum, nor a maximum at $(x_1^0, ..., x_n^0)$.

IV. If Q is zero for some admissible values of its argument, and is of the same sign for all other admissible values $p_1,$ ..., p_n, the question cannot be solved by means of the first and second derivatives (f_i, C_{hi}, f_{ij}, C_{hij}) above.

The characteristic equation in the above case (n variables, m constraints)

The problem which now arises is to find simple criteria which allow us to know when the quadratic form $Q(p_1, ..., p_n)$ will have the properties which correspond to the cases (I)–(IV). These criteria can be formulated by means of the roots of the characteristic equation:

$$(12.22) \quad \begin{vmatrix} (A_{11}-\lambda) & A_{12} & \cdots & A_{1n} & C_{11} & C_{21} \cdots C_{m1} \\ A_{21} & (A_{22}-\lambda) & \cdots & A_{2n} & C_{12} & C_{22} \cdots C_{m2} \\ \cdots\cdots\cdots\cdots\cdots\cdots\cdots\cdots\cdots \\ A_{n1} & A_{n2} & \cdots (A_{nn}-\lambda) & C_{1n} & C_{2n} \cdots C_{mn} \\ C_{11} & C_{12} & \cdots C_{1n} & 0 & 0 & \cdots 0 \\ C_{21} & C_{22} & \cdots C_{2n} & 0 & 0 & \cdots 0 \\ \cdots\cdots\cdots\cdots\cdots\cdots\cdots\cdots\cdots \\ C_{m1} & C_{m2} & \cdots C_{mn} & 0 & 0 & \cdots 0 \end{vmatrix} = 0.$$

All the roots $\lambda_1,$ ..., λ_n of this equation are real since the matrix is real and symmetrical (cf. Theorem (13.60).)

Let λ_{max} and λ_{min} be respectively the greatest and the smallest root of (12.22). Then we have exactly the same criteria for the four cases (I)–(IV) as in (11.4), with the difference that these criteria apply here to the extremum of f subject to the constraints (6.9), while in (11.9) there were no constraints.

One can verify the correctness of the criteria (12.22) in the following way:

When $(p_1 \ldots p_n)$ varies within the bounds of the domain defined by the conditions (12.20)–(12.21), the quadratic form Q defined by (12.17) varies too. If we can find for Q a strictly positive lower bound, or a strictly negative upper bound, we will have a sufficient criterion for the point $(x_1^0, ..., x_n^0)$ to be a constrained minimum, or a constrained maximum respectively. For this, it is not necessary that these bounds should be exact in the sense that Q attains effectively the lower and upper bounds. It is not even necessary that the nature of the restrictions imposed and the

126

structure of Q should be such that Q could approach these bounds as closely as desired. It is enough that the lower bound (or the upper bound) should be truly below (or above) the level of the values which Q is in fact capable of assuming. Provided that the lower bound is strictly positive, and the upper strictly negative, the determination of these bounds will provide us in every case with a sufficient criterion for the point $(x_1^0, \ldots, x_n^0)$ to be a constrained minimum or maximum.

Yet this imprecise determination of the bounds does not permit us to give a really good solution for the problem. The sufficient criteria which we should obtain in this way would be correct, but they would often be "too sufficient" to provide us with any really interesting information. Obviously we would like to be in a position to formulate sufficient criteria which approach the necessary criteria as closely as possible. (On the subject of necessary and sufficient conditions, see the Remarks in the last section of Chapter I). In other words, we are interested in finding the exact bounds of the values taken by Q within the bounds of the domain of variation defined by (12.20)–(12.21).

Does the quadratic form take effectively a maximum value and a minimum value?

If it is the property of the limitations (12.20) – (12.21) and of the quadratic form Q that there exists a maximum value and a minimum value effectively taken by Q, then clearly these extremal values are of the greatest interest to us.

However, not every domain of variation and not every function has the property that the function takes a maximum value and a minimum value as the argument varies over the domain of variation. Let us consider, for example, the function $f(x)$ represented by figure (3.5). If we take an open interval for the domain of variation, we cannot define a value, which would be the greatest value the function $f(x)$ is capable of taking in this domain. This is the case in spite of the fact that the function is bounded in the domain of variation considered, which itself is bounded. In fact we know precisely the exact upper bounds of the values taken by the function: it is clearly $f(b)$. Yet the function never takes the value $f(b)$ in the course of the variation of its argument in the open interval. Furthermore, the same applies to the minimum of the function.

On the other hand, if we take for the domain of variation of x a closed interval (a, b) – still in the figure (3.5) – there exists a maximum value and a minimum value which the function effectively takes in the course of its considered variation.

If we know in advance that there existed a maximum value taken effectively by the quadratic form Q in the course of its variation restricted by (12.20)–(12.21), we could assert that this global maximum also constituted a local maximum $(p_1^0, ..., p_2^0)$ of Q under the conditions imposed. If we knew, moreover, that all the local maxima are points of the region in which the second partial derivatives – with respect to $(p_1, ..., p_n)$ of the function Q and of the equations (12.20)–(12.21) are continuous (and that the same is true for the minima), we could solve the problem – excluding the complications concerning the endpoints of the type indicated by (3.5) – by employing the method expounded in Chapter VI (cf. notably (6.20)). This method consists of writing down the necessary first-order conditions for the local extrema of Q, and then of calculating the value of Q at each point satisfying this criterion and the conditions (12.20)–(12.21). If it turned out that the smallest of the values determined in this way was positive, we should have case (I); if the greatest such value were negative, this would be case (II); and case (III) if the greatest value were positive, and the smallest negative; finally, we should have case (IV) if the greatest or the smallest value were zero.

The fact that the above-mentioned partial derivatives of Q and (12.20)–(12.21) have everywhere continuous derivatives of any order is a trivial consequence of the fact that Q is a quadratic form, that (12.20) is a linear function, and that (12.21) is quadratic in $(p_1, ..., p_n)$. However, it is not clear in advance that Q in fact takes effectively a maximum value and a minimum value as the argument $(p_1, ..., p_n)$ varies in every way compatible with the constraints (12.20)–(12.21). Equally, it is not at once evident that no difficulties will arise concerning the end points.

Provisional analysis on the hypothesis that the values satisfying the first-order conditions are taken by the form and that there are no difficulties concerning the endpoints

However, let us suppose provisionally that we have the desired assurance on these two points. Then nothing is simpler than to obtain the characteristic equation (12.22) and to proceed with its help to a complete analysis of the situation.

In view of (6.20), we obtain a necessary criterion for the local extrema of Q by forming the function

$$(12.23) \quad \varphi(p_1 \ldots p_n) = \sum_{i=1}^{n} \sum_{j=1}^{n} A_{ij} p_i p_j + 2\mu_1 \sum_{i=1}^{n} C_{1i} p_i +$$

$$+ 2\mu_2 \sum_{i=1}^{n} C_{2i} p_i + \cdots + 2\mu_m \sum_{i=1}^{n} C_{mi} p_i - \lambda(p_1^2 + \cdots + p_n^2),$$

where $2\mu_1, 2\mu_2, \ldots, 2\mu_m$, and λ are a set of $(m+1)$ Lagrange multipliers. Here, we cannot use $\lambda_1, \ldots, \lambda_m$ to denote the first m Lagrange multipliers which we need since these symbols have been given above another meaning: they denote the Lagrange multipliers applied to the function f itself, and occurring in the definition (12.18) of the matrix A_{ij}, which we now take as a starting point and which is defined at the point $(x_1^0, \ldots, x_n^0)$. To obtain a sufficient criterion for the extremum of f we have to study the problem in "two distinct stages", as we have seen already in Chapter X. For the moment, let us consider the "second stage" and search for the extrema of the quadratic form Q considered as a function of $(p_1, \ldots, p_n)$.

If we calculate the partial derivatives of (12.23) with respect to p_r $(r = 1, 2, \ldots, n)$ while $\mu_1, \ldots, \mu_m$, and λ, no less than A_{ij} and $C_{1i} \ldots C_{mi}$ are considered as constants (values which depend on the point $(x_1^0, \ldots, x_n^0)$, which is now fixed), and if next we put all the expressions obtained equal to zero, we have the following n linear equations for the $(n+m)$ unknowns $(p_1, p_2, \ldots, p_n; \mu_1, \mu_2, \ldots, \mu_m)$:

$$(12.24) \quad \sum_{j=1}^{n} (A_{ij} - \lambda e_{ij}) p_j + \mu_1 C_{1i} + \mu_2 C_{2i} + \cdots + \mu_m C_{mi} = 0$$

$$(i = 1, 2, \ldots, n)$$

Including the m equations (12.20), we have a total of $(n+m)$ linear equations in the $(n+m)$ unknowns.

These $(n+m)$ linear equations are all homogeneous, i.e. their right-hand sides are identically zero. However, we know that the $(n+m)$ values $(p_1, p_2, \ldots, p_n; \mu_1, \mu_2, \ldots, \mu_m)$ which figure in this linear system cannot be simultaneously zero since $(p_1, \ldots, p_n)$ must satisfy (12.21), which excludes the trivial solution $p_1 = \cdots = p_n = 0$. For a system of $(n+m)$ homogeneous linear equations in $(n+m)$ unknowns to have a non-trivial (nonidentically zero) solution, it is necessary, in virtue of theorem (8.22), that the coefficient-determinant should be zero. This is the necessary condition expressed by (12.22).

We can sum up the preceding discussion in the following form:

THEOREM (12.25). For the existence of a system of values $(p_1, ..., p_n)$ giving a local extremum for the quadratic form Q under the constraints (12.20)–(12.21), it is necessary that there exists a number λ satisfying (12.22). If this is so, the values $(p_1, ..., p_n)$ obtained by solving the linear system (12.20) and (12.24) – after substituting the suitable value of λ – will satisfy the necessary first order conditions for the extremum of Q under the constraints (12.20)–(12.21).

From this we derive also:

THEOREM (12.26). The value taken by the quadratic form Q for the argument $(p_1, ..., p_n)$ determined according to theorem (12.25) is equal to the value λ which satisfies (12.22), and was used to construct the system of linear equations (12.20) and (12.24).

In fact, if we multiply (12.24) by p_i and sum with respect to i, we obtain

$$(12.27) \qquad \lambda \sum_{i=1}^{n} \sum_{j=1}^{n} e_{ij}p_i p_j = \sum_{i=1}^{n} \sum_{j=1}^{n} A_{ij}p_i p_j + \sum_{h=1}^{m} \mu_h \sum_{i=1}^{n} C_{hi}p_i.$$

The double sum on the left-hand side of (12.27) reduces to 1 in virtue of (12.21), while on the right-hand side the first double sum is simply the quadratic form $Q(p_1, ..., p_n)$, and the second sum is zero in view of (12.20).

Thus, if we could be certain that Q takes effectively a maximum value and a minimum value in the domain considered, and that no difficulties arise in regard to the end points, we could conclude from the preceding discussion – in view of what we know of the local extrema of the function f under the constraints (6.9) – that we are entitled to formulate the sufficient criteria in complete analogy with (11.4), with the only difference that the roots λ_{max} and λ_{min} are now the roots of (12.22).

Thus, it only remains to answer the two questions which we have raised above concerning the values taken effectively by Q, and concerning the end points.

Graphical analysis tending to show that the hypothesis is confirmed

We consider first a graphical representation of the case where $n=3$ and $m=1$. Figure (12.28) shows a three-dimensional space (p_1, p_2, p_3). The sphere of radius 1 constructed around the origin represents the condition

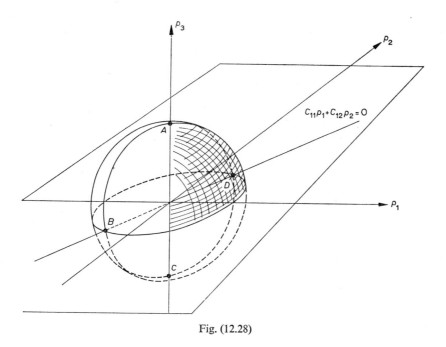

Fig. (12.28)

(12.21). It corresponds to the circle $ABCD$ of figure (10.10) with the difference that there we have entered on the diagram the values of the quadratic form itself, while figure (12.28) represents only the domain of variation of the argument.

The plane passing through the origin, and intersecting the sphere in the great circle $ABCD$ represents the homogeneous linear equation $C_{11}p_1 + C_{12}p_2 + C_{13}p_3 = 0$. We have put $C_{13} = 0$ in order that the plane should be perpendicular to the plane (p_1, p_2). Hence it is the great circle $ABCD$ which represents the domain of the argument (p_1, p_2, p_3).

131

Thus we will study in this domain the variation of the quadratic form

(12.29)
$$Q(p_1, p_2, p_3) = \sum_{i=1}^{3} \sum_{j=1}^{3} A_{ij} p_i p_j.$$

It is clear that if A_{ij} are given numbers (constants under the variation of (p_1, p_2, p_3)), Q must have a well defined value at every point of the great circle, and – since the relation between Q and the variables (p_1, p_2, p_3) is given by a quadratic form – that Q must vary continuously as the argument describes the great circle. It is intuitively clear that, as the argument describes this circle, Q must necessarily pass through a maximum value and a minimum value. Moreover, we see that since the variation of Q and its derivatives are continuous, the ordinary first-order conditions will be fulfilled for these extrema. No particular problem arises concerning the end points.

Thus, insofar as Q takes effectively its maximum and minimum values, the situation is the same as when, in figure (3.5), we considered the interval as closed. Nevertheless, there is an essential difference: in figure (3.5) – where the interval is considered as closed to guarantee that the function takes its maximal and minimal value – there exist end points which may be extrema without $f(x)$ satisfying the first-order necessary conditions, which requires that the first derivative should be zero.

It is intuitively clear that this complication does not arise in connection with figure (12.28), or in connection with the general case of a quadratic form of n variables whose argument complies with the conditions (12.20)–(12.21). In fact, the existence of the end points in figure (3.5) is due to the fact that the interval is defined by means of inequalities, while the domain of variation of the argument (in the case of the quadratic form Q) is defined by means of equations only – in general by (12.20)–(12.21) – whose left-hand sides have continuous partial derivatives of all appropriate orders.

The comparison between figures (12.28) and (3.5) also illustrates another important fact:

In both figures the domain of variation is bounded, i.e. all the variables have absolute values which remain bounded. To achieve this in the case of a function of one variable, it is necessary to introduce inequalities in order to avoid the complications relating to the endpoints. On the other hand, in figure (12.28), where there are several variables, the domain can be bounded without causing complications of this kind. In fact, going always in the same direction and not leaving a bounded domain, we can return to our point of departure without "stumbling" against end points.

Exact analysis confirming the hypothesis

Examination of figure (12.28) suggests that a quadratic form Q, subjected to equations of the type (12.20)–(12.21), takes effectively a maximum value and a minimum value in the domain considered, and that moreover these maxima and minima satisfy the ordinary first-order conditions. In order to verify rigorously that this is in fact so, we shall refer to some of the fundamental theorems and definitions of set-theory.

DEFINITION (12.30). By a point of an n-dimensional space we understand a system of n real numbers $(X_1, ..., X_n)$. A set of points, or simply a set, is a collection composed of a finite or infinite number of points.

DEFINITION (12.31). Let E be a given set. Let us assume that there exists a denumerable sequence of points $(x_{1k}, ..., x_{nk})$ $k=1, 2, ..., \infty$ belonging to E (allowing that the same point can be repeated arbitrarily often), and tending towards a point $(X_1, ..., X_n)$ in the sense that to every arbitrarily small positive ε, there corresponds an integer K such that for every $k \geqslant K$ we will have $|x_{ik} - X_i| \leqslant \varepsilon$ for every $i = 1, 2, ..., n$. Then we will say that $(X_1, ..., X_n)$ is a limit-point of the set E.

This limit-point may or may not belong to the set E. If, for example, we consider the set of all points x which belong to the open interval (a, b) in figure (3.5), we see that a is a limit-point of the set, but it does not belong to it. On the other hand, every point situated within the interval is a limit-point of the set, and at the same time, belongs to it.

DEFINITION (12.32). A set which contains all its limit-points is called a closed set.

In figure (3.5), the points contained in the closed interval form a closed set, but not those situated in the open interval. The points situated on a circle, or on some other closed curve in the two dimensional plane (x_1, x_2) form a closed set; the same is true for the points situated on an arc, on the condition that the endpoints of the arc are included.

DEFINITION (12.33). The collection of all the limit-points of a given set form the closure of this set.

Starting from these definitions, one can say that a closed set is a set which contains its closure.

DEFINITION (12.34). To say that a set of points $(x_1, ..., x_n)$ is bounded means that there exist n numbers $M_1, ..., M_n$ such that for each point of the set the absolute value of x_i is at most equal to M_i $(i=1, 2, ..., n)$. And here is an important theorem of set-theory:

THEOREM (12.35). A function continuous at every point of a bounded closed set attains effectively a maximum value and a minimum value as its argument varies over the whole set.

Example: the function $f(x)$ in figure (3.5), where x varies in the closed interval between a and b. Other examples: a continuous function of two variables when the point (x_1, x_2) varies along a circle in the (x_1, x_2) plane, or a continuous function of three variables (x_1, x_2, x_3) when the point (x_1, x_2, x_3) varies on a sphere in the (x_1, x_2, x_3) space.

In order to obtain a definition covering the most general case, we will consider a function having a finite value at an isolated point as continuous at that point (A point is said to be isolated when there exists a neighbourhood of the point containing no other points of the set).

DEFINITION (12.36). An accumulation point of a set is a point $(x_1, x_2, ..., x_n)$ such that every neighbourhood of this point contains an infinite number of points belonging to the above set. That is, for every strictly positive ε, however small, there exists an infinite number of points $(x_1, ..., x_n)$ belonging to the set which satisfy $|x_i - X_i| \leq \varepsilon$ for $i=1, 2, ..., n$.

DEFINITION (12.37). The set of all accumulation points of a given set is called the derived set.

There is a close connection between the concept of an accumulation point and that of a limit point, but they are not identical. It is the concept of a limit point and the concept of a closed set which will be of the greatest interest to us. In particular, theorem (12.35) is based on these concepts.

Starting from the above definitions and theorems, it is now easy to verify that every limit point of the points $(p_1, ..., p_n)$ satisfying (12.20)–(12.21), itself necessarily belongs to this set.

In fact, let $(P_1, ..., P_n)$ be a limit-point of the set we are considering, and let $(p_{1k}, ..., p_{nk})$ $(k=1, 2, ...)$ be a sequence of points belonging to (12.20)–(12.21) and converging to $(P_1, ..., P_n)$. For any positive ε, however small, it is possible to find a number K such that

134

(12.38) $\quad |p_{ik} - P_i| \leqslant \varepsilon \quad$ for $\quad i = 1, 2 \ldots n \quad$ and all $\quad k \geqslant K$.

Since all the $(p_{1k}, \ldots, p_{nk})$ belong to (12.20), we have for every k

$$\sum_{i=1}^{n} C_{hi} P_i = \sum_{i=1}^{n} C_{hi}(P_i - p_{ik}).$$

Consequently, for all $k \geqslant K$

$$\left(\sum_{i=1}^{n} C_{hi} P_i \right)^2 = \sum_{i=1}^{n} \sum_{j=1}^{n} C_{hi} C_{hj} (P_i - p_{ik})(P_j - p_{jk}) \leqslant \varepsilon^2 \sum_{i=1}^{n} \sum_{j=1}^{n} |C_{hi}| \cdot |C_{hj}|,$$

i.e.

(12.39) $$\left(\sum_{i=1}^{n} C_{hi} P_i \right)^2 \leqslant \varepsilon^2 \left(\sum_{i=1}^{n} |C_{hi}| \right)^2.$$

Since ε can be taken to be as small as we wish, the right-hand side of (12.39) will itself be as small as we wish. Thus (12.39) is valid only if

(12.40) $$\sum_{i=1}^{n} C_{hi} P_i = 0;$$

in other words, $(P_1, \ldots, P_n)$ must satisfy (12.20).

On the other hand, we have for every k

$$\sum_{i=1}^{n} P_i^2 = \sum_{i=1}^{n} \left[(P_i - p_{ik})^2 + 2p_{ik}(P_i - p_{ik}) + p_{ik}^2 \right]$$

$$= 1 + \sum_{i=1}^{n} \left[(P_i - p_{ik})^2 + 2p_{ik}(P_i - p_{ik}) \right].$$

Thus, for every k

$$\left(\sum_{i=1}^{n} P_i^2 - 1 \right)^2 =$$

$$= \sum_{i=1}^{n} \sum_{j=1}^{n} \left[(P_i - p_{ik})^2 + 2p_{ik}(P_i - p_{ik}) \right] \left[(P_j - p_{jk})^2 + 2p_{jk}(P_j - p_{jk}) \right]$$

$$= \sum_{i=1}^{n} \sum_{j=1}^{n} \left\{ (P_i - p_{ik})^2 (P_j - p_{jk})^2 + 2 \left[p_{ik}(P_i - p_{ik})(P_j - p_{jk})^2 + \right. \right.$$

$$\left. \left. + p_{jk}(P_j - p_{jk})(P_i - p_{ik})^2 \right] + 4 p_{ik} p_{jk} (P_i - p_{ik})(P_j - p_{jk}) \right\}.$$

Consequently, for every $k \geqslant K$

(12.41) $$\left(\sum_{i=1}^{n} P_i^2 - 1 \right)^2 \leqslant n^2 \varepsilon^4 + 4\varepsilon^3 n \sum_{i=1}^{n} |p_{ik}| + 4\varepsilon^2 \left(\sum_{i=1}^{n} |p_{ik}| \right)^2.$$

Since all the coefficients of the powers of ε on the right-hand side are bounded, the right-hand side of (12.41) can be made as small as we wish. Thus (12.41) is valid only if

$$(12.42) \qquad\qquad \sum_{i=1}^{n} P_i^2 = 1 .$$

In other words, $(P_1, \ldots, P_n)$ must also satisfy (12.21), i.e. it belongs itself to the set of points satisfying (12.20)–(12.21). * This set is clearly bounded, since it follows from (12.21) that none of the values $p_1, p_2, \ldots, p_n$ can exceed 1 in absolute value. In other words, the set of points $(p_1, \ldots, p_n)$ which satisfy (12.20)–(12.21) is closed and bounded at the same time. Moreover, the function $Q(p_1, \ldots, p_n)$ is continuous. Now, it follows from theorem (12.35) that – as its argument varies in the domain defined by (12.20)–(12.21) – $Q(p_1, \ldots, p_n)$ effectively attains a maximum value and a minimum value. The points at which Q attains these values are clearly not only global extrema but also local extrema and, since the domain is defined by equations alone, there are no complications concerning endpoints. In other words, the necessary first-order conditions are necessarily fulfilled at the points of maximum and minimum.

In this way, as we have assumed, there exists effectively a number λ which is the root of equation (12.22). Likewise, it is confirmed that the greatest and smallest roots of this equation – which must be real – represent respectively the greatest and the smallest values taken by the quadratic form $Q(p_1, \ldots, p_n)$ in the domain of variation defined by (12.20)–(12.21).

In consequence, in the present case (the case of a function of several variables subject to a number of equational constraints) we have at our disposal again sufficient criteria for the extrema of f, criteria which are completely similar to the criteria stated in (11.4).

EXAMPLES

EXAMPLE (12.1′).

Let us begin by giving a very simple example where one can outline, completely naturally and without analytical complications, the method of calculating the increment

---

* Similarly, we could not say, in (3.5) for example, whether we were taking the interval as open.

of a quantity starting from a position which satisfies the necessary conditions for an extremum. Because of its simple form, we can recognise whether or not this increment preserves a fixed sign, and hence we can solve the extremum problem without making full use of the theory of Chapter XII.

Let us now search for the extremum of the function

$$f(x_1, x_2) \equiv x_1 x_2$$

when x_1 and x_2 are subjected to the constraint

$$0 = C(x_1, x_2) \equiv x_1 + x_2 - a = 0$$

a being a constant.

We obtain the necessary conditions by considering

$$f + \lambda C \equiv x_1 x_2 + \lambda (x_1 + x_2 - a)$$

and looking for the conditions under which

$$f'_{x_1} + \lambda C'_{x_1} = f'_{x_2} + \lambda C'_{x_2} = 0$$

Taking $x_1 + x_2 - a = 0$ into account, we must have

$$\begin{cases} f'_{x_1} + \lambda C'_{x_1} \equiv x_2 + \lambda = 0 \\ f'_{x_2} + \lambda C'_{x_2} \equiv x_1 + \lambda = 0 \\ \qquad\qquad x_1 + x_2 - a = 0 \end{cases}$$

It is clear that $\lambda = -x_1 = -x_2$. Hence

and

$$x_1^0 = x_2^0 \quad \text{and consequently} \quad = \frac{a}{2}.$$

$$\lambda = -\frac{a}{2}.$$

Let us put now

$$x_1 = x_1^0 + \varDelta x_1$$
$$x_2 = x_2^0 + \varDelta x_2$$

Then we have that

$$x_1 x_2 = (x_1^0 + \varDelta x_1)(x_2^0 + \varDelta x_2) = x_1^0 x_2^0 + (\varDelta x_2 x_1^0 + \varDelta x_1 x_2^0 + \varDelta x_1 \varDelta x_2)$$

and

$$= \frac{a^2}{4} + \frac{a}{2}\varDelta x_1 + \frac{a}{2}\varDelta x_2 + \varDelta x_1 \varDelta x_2.$$

$$x_1 + x_2 - a = 0 \equiv \frac{a}{2} + \varDelta x_1 + \frac{a}{2} + \varDelta x_2 - a = 0$$

or

$$\varDelta x_1 + \varDelta x_2 = 0 \quad \varDelta x_2 = -\varDelta x_1.$$

Thus one verifies that because of the condition the terms in $\varDelta x_1$ and $\varDelta x_2$ vanish from $x_1 x_2$, and we are left with

$$x_1 x_2 = \frac{a^2}{4} - (\varDelta x_1)^2.$$

From this last form it is clear that $x_1 x_2$ has an effective maximum for $\Delta x_1 = 0$, since every non-zero value of Δx_1 must lower the value of the right-hand side.

In conclusion: the product of two variables whose sum is constant is maximal (and not only in the local sense) when the two variables are equal (and consequently each is equal to the half of their sum).

EXAMPLE (12.2').

We will generalize the preceding example by keeping the constraint

$$C(x_1, x_2) = x_1 + x_2 - a = 0$$

but taking a slightly more complicated function which gives us more varied results. This function is

$$f_2(x_1, x_2) = x_1^\alpha x_2^\beta$$

where α and β are integral exponents which, for the sake of simplicity, we take to be positive. We shall exclude *a priori* the case when one of the two or both are zero, because in this case the problem would reduce to a problem in one variable.

Under these conditions, the first-order necessary conditions can be written down by differentiating $x_1^\alpha x_2^\beta + \mu(x_1 + x_2 - a)$ and adjoining the constraint $C(x_1, x_2) = 0$.

$$\begin{cases} \alpha x_1^{\alpha-1} x_2^\beta + \mu = 0 \\ \beta x_1^\alpha x_2^{\beta-1} + \mu = 0 \\ x_1 + x_2 - a = 0 \end{cases}$$

This is equivalent to

$$\begin{cases} \mu = -\alpha x_1^{\alpha-1} x_2^\beta \\ \alpha x_1^{\alpha-1} x_2^\beta = \beta x_1^\alpha x_2^{\beta-1} \\ x_1 + x_2 - a = 0 \end{cases}$$

or

$$\begin{cases} \mu = -\alpha x_1^{\alpha-1} x_2^\beta \\ \alpha x_2 = \beta x_1 \quad \text{if} \quad x_1 x_2 \neq 0 \\ x_1 + x_2 - a = 0 \end{cases}$$

If now $x_1 x_2 \neq 0$, one has

$$\frac{x_1}{\alpha} = \frac{x_2}{\beta} = \frac{x_1 + x_2}{\alpha + \beta} = \frac{a}{\alpha + \beta} \quad \text{if} \quad \alpha + \beta \neq 0.$$

Hence the solution for the extremum

$$\begin{cases} x_1^0 = a \dfrac{\alpha}{\alpha + \beta} \\[2em] x_2^0 = a \dfrac{\beta}{\alpha + \beta} \\[2em] \mu^0 = -\dfrac{\alpha^\alpha \beta^\beta}{(\alpha + \beta)^{(\alpha+\beta-1)}} a^{\alpha+\beta-1}. \end{cases}$$

We put now

$$x_1 = x_1^0 + \Delta x_1, \quad x_2 = x_2^0 + \Delta x_2.$$

Then

$$
\begin{aligned}
f_2(x_1, x_2) = x_1^\alpha x_2^\beta = {}& f_2(x_1^0, x_2^0) + \Delta x_1\,\alpha x_1^{0\alpha-1} x_2^{0\beta} + \Delta x_2\,\beta x_1^{0\alpha} x_2^{0\beta-1} \\
& + \Delta x_1^2\,\alpha(\alpha-1) x_1^{0\alpha-2} x_2^{0\beta} + 2\Delta x_1 \Delta x_2\,\alpha\beta\, x_1^{0\alpha-1} x_2^{0\beta-1} \\
& + \Delta x_2^2\,\beta(\beta-1) x_1^{0\alpha} x_2^{0\beta-2} + \cdots
\end{aligned}
$$

$C(x_1, x_2)$ gives again $\Delta x_1 + \Delta x_2 = 0$, whence

$$
\begin{aligned}
f_2(x_1, x_2) = {}& \frac{\alpha^\alpha \beta^\beta}{(\alpha+\beta)^{\alpha+\beta}}\, a^{\alpha+\beta} + \Delta x_1\,[\alpha x_1^{0\alpha-1} x_2^{0\beta} - \beta x_1^{0\alpha} x_2^{0\beta-1}] \\
& + \Delta x_1^2\,[\alpha(\alpha-1) x_1^{0\alpha-2} x_2^{0\beta} - 2\alpha\beta x_1^{0\alpha-1} x_2^{0\beta-1} + \beta(\beta-1) x_1^{0\alpha} x_2^{0\beta-2}] + \cdots
\end{aligned}
$$

where the three dots stand for terms which are negligible locally. Thus

$$
\begin{aligned}
f_2(x_1, x_2) = {}& \frac{\alpha^\alpha \beta^\beta}{(\alpha+\beta)^{\alpha+\beta}}\, a^{(\alpha+\beta)} \\
& + \Delta x_1^2\, x_1^{0(\alpha-2)} x_2^{0(\beta-2)}\,[\alpha(\alpha-1)(x_2^0)^2 - 2\alpha\beta x_1^0 x_2^0 + \beta(\beta-1)(x_1^0)^2] + \cdots
\end{aligned}
$$

The study of the extremum thus reduces to examining the sign of

$$
[\alpha(\alpha-1)(x_2^0)^2 - 2\alpha\beta\, x_1^0 x_2^0 + \beta(\beta-1)(x_1^0)^2]\frac{a^{\alpha+\beta-4}\,\alpha^{\alpha-2}\beta^{\beta-2}}{(\alpha+\beta)^{\alpha+\beta-4}}
$$

$$
= \frac{a^{\alpha+\beta-2}}{(\alpha+\beta)^{\alpha+\beta-2}}\,[\alpha(\alpha-1)\beta^2 - 2\alpha^2\beta^2 + \beta(\beta-1)\alpha^2]\,\alpha^{\alpha-2}\beta^{\beta-2}
$$

which has the sign of $-\alpha^{\alpha-1}\beta^{\beta-1} a^{\alpha+\beta-2}/(\alpha+\beta)^{\alpha+\beta-3}$ or again of $-a^{\alpha+\beta}$ since α and β are assumed to be positive. Thus

(1) If a is positive, $-a^{\alpha+\beta}$ is negative.
(2) If a is negative, the sign of $-a^{\alpha+\beta}$ depends on the parity of $\alpha + \beta$:
(2a) If $\alpha + \beta$ is even, $-a^{\alpha+\beta}$ is negative.
(2b) If $\alpha + \beta$ is odd, $-a^{\alpha+\beta}$ is positive.

In consequence, we have a maximum unless a is negative and $\alpha + \beta$ is odd (that is when α and β have different parities), in which case we have a minimum.

Another method

If we apply the more theoretical method of Chapter XII, we obtain the equation in λ

$$
\begin{vmatrix}
\alpha(\alpha-1) x_1^{0\alpha-2} x_2^{0\beta} - \lambda & \alpha\beta\, x_1^{0\alpha-1} x_2^{0\beta-1} & 1 \\
\alpha\beta\, x_1^{0\alpha-1} x_2^{0\beta-1} & \beta(\beta-1) x_1^{0\alpha} x_2^{0\beta-2} - \lambda & 1 \\
1 & 1 & 0
\end{vmatrix} = 0
$$

$$\left(\text{since } \frac{\partial C}{\partial x_1} = \frac{\partial C}{\partial x_2} = 1 \text{ here}\right)$$

or

$$- [\alpha (\alpha - 1) x_1^{0\alpha-2} x_2^{0\beta} - \lambda] + 2\alpha\beta x_1^{0\alpha-1} x_2^{0\beta-1} - [\beta (\beta - 1) x_1^{0\alpha} x_2^{0\beta-2} - \lambda] = 0$$

or

$$2\lambda = x_1^{0\alpha-2} x_2^{0\beta-2} [\alpha (\alpha - 1) (x_2^0)^2 - 2\alpha\beta x_1^0 x_2^0 + \beta (\beta - 1) (x_1^0)^2]$$

$$= \frac{a^{\alpha+\beta-2}}{(\alpha + \beta)^{\alpha+\beta-2}} \alpha^{\alpha-2} \beta^{\beta-2} [\alpha (\alpha - 1) \beta^2 - 2\alpha\beta\alpha\beta + \beta (\beta - 1) \alpha^2]$$

$$= - a^{\alpha+\beta-2} \left[\frac{\alpha^{\alpha-1} \beta^{\beta-1}}{(\alpha + \beta)^{\alpha+\beta-3}} \right].$$

The discussion on the nature of the extremum based on the sign of λ is thus, naturally, exactly identical to what we did above.

We leave it to the reader to study directly what happens in the case when x_1 and x_2 tend to infinity, a case which is generally overlooked, because the usual reasoning assumes that one is considering a finite point, but which can be of concrete interest in a given problem which requires the investigation of the boundary points. Further, we have implicitly excluded the case when $x_1 + x_2 = 0$ but we expressly ask the reader to discuss this case as an exercise.

EXAMPLE (12.3′).

We shall now give a type of example which is often encountered in economic analysis. This example is drawn from a simple case of profit-maximization under given constraints.

One assumes that the production of a certain good is represented by an equation of the form

$$f = zx$$

where f is the quantity produced, z expresses the volume of the factor of production equipment and x is the quantity of the labour used.

One assumes that one has the sum of money d at one's disposal, and that the price of the unit of labour is $p = p_0 + \varpi_0 (2N - x)^{-1}$ ($p_0 > 0, \varpi_0 > 0$) and that the unit-price of the equipment is constant and equal to r_0. We will here suppose that the equipment is bought to this fixed price and subsequently worne out to zero value during the production process considered. One wants to determine x and z in such a way that the value of the production (f) should be maximum for the sum d spent, keeping also in mind that the availability of the man-power is limited by N (thus $0 \leqslant x \leqslant N$).

This example will serve not only to illustrate the theory of Chapter XII, but also to show how the end-points can intervene in the consideration of maxima (or, in other cases, minima).

If we set aside at first the end-points, the problem consists of maximizing the function

$$f = zx$$

taking into account the expense-relation

(1) $$C_1 = px + r_0 z - d = 0$$

(Using a type of argument which we have often come across already, it is easy to see that, apart from the end-points, it is always in our interest to use up all the money available.) and the price-relation

(2)
$$C_2 = p - p_0 - \frac{\varpi_0}{2N - x} = 0.$$

The variables are x, z, p and are subject to the restraints (1) and (2). We will denote the multipliers attached to (1) and (2) by μ_1 and μ_2 respectively.

The equations of the extremum are obtained by differentiating the function

$$zx + \mu_1 [px + r_0 z - d] + \mu_2 \left[p - p_0 - \frac{\varpi_0}{2N - x} \right]$$

successively with respect to x, z, p and putting the derivatives equal to zero, taking (1) and (2) also into account. The differentiations give:

$$\frac{\partial}{\partial x}: \quad z + \mu_1 p - \mu_2 \frac{\varpi_0}{(2N - x)^2} = 0$$

$$\frac{\partial}{\partial z}: \quad x + \mu_1 r_0 = 0$$

$$\frac{\partial}{\partial p}: \quad \mu_1 x + \mu_2 = 0.$$

Hence $\mu_2 = - \mu_1 x$ and substituting into the preceding two equations

$$z + \mu_1 \left[p + \frac{x \varpi_0}{(2N - x)^2} \right] = 0$$

$$x + \mu_1 r_0 = 0.$$

Since these two equations in μ_1 must be compatible, one concludes that the matrix of the coefficients and constant terms must be of rank 1, which is equivalent to condition (3) in x and z:

(3)
$$\begin{vmatrix} z & p + \dfrac{x \varpi_0}{(2N - x)^2} \\ x & r_0 \end{vmatrix} = 0$$

which, together with (1) and (2) determines $x, z,$ and p.

Condition (3) is, more specifically, a condition of extremum; it defines z (we will denote it by z_e) as a function of x, by the formula:

$$z_e = \frac{x}{r_0} \left[p + \frac{x \varpi_0}{(2N - x)^2} \right] = \frac{x}{r_0} \left[p_0 + \frac{2N \varpi_0}{(2N - x)^2} \right].$$

(1) defines z (which we denote by z_d)

$$z_d = \frac{d}{r_0} - \frac{px}{r_0} = \frac{d}{r_0} - \frac{x}{r_0} \left[p_0 + \frac{\varpi_0}{2N - x} \right].$$

The extremum will be attained when $z_e = z_d$, provided that the corresponding value of x is between 0 and N.

Now one can see immediately that z_e is an increasing function of x between 0 and N, and that z_d is a decreasing function in the same interval (since p is an increasing function of x). Moreover, for $x = 0$, z_e is zero and z_d is positive. Thus, one can have a point of extremum (and only one) if and only if either

$$z_e (N) \geqslant z_d (N)$$

$$\frac{N}{r_0}\left[p_0 + \frac{2\varpi_0}{N}\right] \geqslant \frac{d}{r_0} - \frac{N}{r_0}\left[p_0 + \frac{\varpi_0}{N}\right]$$

or

(4) $$d \leqslant 2 N p_0 + 3\varpi_0.$$

1. If this condition (4) is fulfilled, let us denote by x_0 the abscissa of the extremum, while z_0 is derived for example from

$$z_0 = \frac{x_0}{r_0}\left[p_0 + \frac{2 N \varpi_0}{2 (N - x_0)^2}\right].$$

The determination of x_0 leads to the solution of a cubic equation, but for the discussion we need not know its exact value explicitly.

We deduce that

$$\mu_1 = - \frac{x_0}{r_0}$$

$$\mu_2 = \frac{x_0^2}{r_0}.$$

Taking the values of C_{ij} into account, the equation in λ determining the nature of the extremum will have the following form:

$$\begin{vmatrix} -\dfrac{2x_0^2 \varpi_0}{r_0 (2N - x_0)^3} - \lambda & 1 & -\dfrac{x_0}{r_0} & p & -\dfrac{\varpi_0}{(2 N - x_0)^2} \\ 1 & -\lambda & 0 & r_0 & 0 \\ -\dfrac{x_0}{r_0} & 0 & -\lambda & x_0 & 1 \\ p & r_0 & x_0 & 0 & 0 \\ -\dfrac{\varpi_0}{(2 N - x_0)^2} & 0 & 1 & 0 & 0 \end{vmatrix} = 0$$

142

i.e.

$$\left[-\frac{2x_0{}^2\varpi_0}{r_0\,(2N-x_0)^3}-\lambda\right]r_0{}^2-r_0\left[p+\frac{x_0\varpi_0}{(2\,N-x_0)^2}\right]-x_0\frac{r_0\varpi_0}{(2\,N-x_0)^2}$$

$$+p\left[-r_0-\lambda\left(p+\frac{x_0\varpi_0}{(2\,N-x_0)^2}\right)\right]-\frac{\varpi_0 x_0}{(2\,N-x_0)^2}\left[r_0+\lambda\left(p+\frac{x_0\varpi_0}{(2\,N-x_0)^2}\right)\right]$$

$$+\frac{\varpi_0 r_0}{(2\,N-x_0)^2}\left[-x_0-\frac{r_0\varpi_0\lambda}{(2\,N-x_0)^2}\right]=0$$

or

$$\lambda\left[r_0{}^2+\left[p+\frac{x_0\varpi_0}{(2\,N-x_0)^2}\right]^2+\frac{\varpi_0{}^2 r_0{}^2}{(2\,N-x_0)^4}\right]$$

$$=\lambda\left[r_0{}^2+\left(p_0+\frac{2\,N\varpi_0}{(2\,N-x_0)^2}\right)^2+\frac{\varpi_0{}^2 r_0{}^2}{(2\,N-x_0)^4}\right]$$

$$=-\left[\frac{2x_0{}^2\varpi_0 r_0}{(2\,N-x_0)^3}+2r_0\left(p_0+\frac{2\,N\varpi_0}{(2\,N-x_0)^2}\right)+\frac{2x_0 r_0\varpi_0}{(2\,N-x_0)^2}\right].$$

Thus

$$\lambda=\frac{-r_0\left[2p_0+\frac{4\,N\varpi_0+2x_0\varpi_0}{(2\,N-x_0)^2}+\frac{2x_0{}^2\varpi_0}{(2\,N-x_0)^3}\right]}{r_0{}^2+\left[p_0+\frac{2\,N\varpi_0}{(2\,N-x_0)^2}\right]^2+\frac{\varpi_0{}^2 r_0{}^2}{(2\,N-x_0)^4}}.$$

It is obvious that the numerator of λ is negative and its denominator is positive. Hence λ is negative and we have an effective maximum.

2. If the condition (4) is not fulfilled, this is because the sum of money is too large in proportion to the available man-power; the reader can easily verify that in this case the value of x_0 is contained between N and $2N$. It is intuitively clear that we have to look for the extremum in one of the end-points, that is one of the two values $x=0$, or $x=N$. The first one clearly has to be discarded since f would be zero. The second gives $x_0=N$. z is given by z_d alone, since it is no longer possible to have a local extremum, and thus

$$z_0=\frac{d}{r_0}-\frac{Np_0}{r_0}-\frac{\varpi_0}{r_0}$$

Finally, the maximal value of f is given by

$$x_0 z_0=\frac{N}{r_0}[d-Np_0-\varpi_0].$$

A BRIEF ACCOUNT OF THE THEORY
OF MATRICES AND OF
THE CALCULATION OF DETERMINANTS

In order to clarify the material presented in the other chapters, we shall introduce here some elementary concepts concerning the theory of matrices and determinants.

Definition of a matrix and examination of the special case of square matrices

A matrix is simply a table of numbers arranged in rows and columns, in the following way:

(13.1)
$$\left\|\begin{array}{cccc} a_{11}a_{12} & \cdots\cdots & a_{1n} \\ a_{21}a_{22} & \cdots\cdots & a_{2n} \\ \cdot\quad\cdot\quad\cdot\quad\cdot\quad\cdot\quad\cdot \\ a_{m1}a_{m2} & \cdots\cdots & a_{mn} \end{array}\right\|$$

The values a_{ij} $(i=1, 2, ..., m; j=1, 2, ..., n)$ are the elements of the matrix. The matrix (13.1) has m rows numbered $i=1, 2, ..., m$ and n columns numbered $j=1, 2, ..., n$. In the general formulation we do not assume anything concerning the numbers m and n. We can have $m \gtreqless n$.

The two double bars on each side of the matrix signify that we consider all the $m \cdot n$ values as a complex, where the place of each element is determined.

In the particular case when $m=n$, we speak of a square matrix.

To distinguish this special case, we shall enclose the table not between two double bars as in (13.1), but between two large parentheses, as below:

(13.2)
$$\left(\begin{array}{cccc} a_{11}a_{12} & \cdots\cdots & a_{1n} \\ a_{12}a_{22} & \cdots\cdots & a_{2n} \\ \cdot\quad\cdot\quad\cdot\quad\cdot\quad\cdot\quad\cdot \\ a_{n1}a_{n2} & \cdots\cdots & a_{nn} \end{array}\right)$$

By the order of a square matrix we mean the number of its rows – and consequently the number of its columns. In this way we speak of matrices of order 2, of matrices of order 3, etc.

For the sake of convenience we shall agree that the symbol $\|a\|$ denotes a matrix of the type (13.1) and the symbol (a) a matrix of the type (13.2). In the same way, we write $\|b\|$ or (b) to denote matrices formed by means of the elements b_{ij} instead of a_{ij}. This symbolism will help us to remember that a matrix must be conceived as an entity in itself, which has certain properties which deserve to be studied.

It is sometimes convenient to have a particular symbol to denote "the element ij of the matrix $\|a\|$". We represent it by $\|a\|_{ij}$. We shall use $(a)_{ij}$ in the analogous sense. When the matrices are written in the explicit form (13.1) and (13.2), the above symbols denote simply the element a_{ij}. In some cases, however, the notation $\|a\|_{ij}$ or $(a)_{ij}$ is practical, notably when the matrix $\|a\|$ or (a) is defined in a less explicit form than (13.1) or (13.2). We shall meet such examples later.

We denote by $\|a\|_{)ij(}$ or $(a)_{)ij(}$ the matrix obtained by suppressing in $\|a\|$ or (a) the i-th row and the j-th column. In (13.20)–(13.21) we shall find an example of this symbolism.

To distinguish the matrices, we shall refer to ordinary numbers as scalars.

Symbolic operations on matrices

We shall define some of the simpler rules of symbolic operations concerning the matrices. In the rest of this chapter when we speak of "matrices" without further qualification we shall mean square matrices, unless the context contradicts this accepted meaning. We shall specify explicitly everywhere where it is necessary whether we are talking of a square matrix or of a matrix which may or may not be square. In practice, every proposition which is applicable to matrices in general is also valid for square matrices.

DEFINITION (13.3). Multiplying a matrix (square or not) by a scalar number means the formation of a new matrix in which each element is equal to the corresponding element of the original matrix multiplied by the scalar in question. That is: $\|\gamma a\|_{ij} = \gamma \|a_{ij}\|$.

DEFINITION (13.4). The sum of two matrices (square or not) is defined as a matrix in which each element is the sum of the corresponding elements of the two initial matrices. That is:

$$\{\|a\| + \|b\|\}_{ij} = \|a\|_{ij} + \|b\|_{ij}.$$

We can define in the same way the sum of several matrices, for example $\|a\| + \|b\| + \|c\|$. We see at once that this sum is associative in the sense that it can be conceived as $\{\|a\| + \|b\|\} + \|c\|$ as well as $\|a\| + \{\|b\| + \|c\|\}$.

DEFINITION (13.5). When $\|a\|$ and $\|b\|$ denote two matrices which have the same number of rows and the same number of columns, the matrix relation $\|a\| = \|b\|$ means that each element of $\|a\|$ is equal to the corresponding element of $\|b\|$, i.e. $\|a\|_{ij} = \|b\|_{ij}$ for all i and j.

DEFINITION (13.6). By the product of two matrices (a) and (b) – in symbols: $(a) \cdot (b)$ – we mean the square matrix whose element ij is the sum of the products of the elements of the i-th row of (a) with the elements of the j-th column of (b). In other words,

$$\{(a) \cdot (b)\}_{ij} = \sum_k a_{ik} b_{kj},$$

where k runs through the values: 1, 2, ..., n, if n is the order of (a) and (b).

When $(a) = (b)$, their product is called the symbolic square of (a), and is denoted by $(a)^2$.

The product of matrices defined by (13.6) is not commutative, i.e. the order of factors is, in general, not irrelevant. In other words, in general $(a) \cdot (b) \neq (b) \cdot (a)$. In fact, by definition

$$\{(b) \cdot (a)\}_{ij} = \sum_k b_{ik} a_{kj}$$

and this is not necessarily the same as $\sum_k a_{ik} b_{kj}$. Thus when we consider matrices we must distinguish between a right-multiplier and a left-multiplier.

When the matrix $(a) \cdot (b)$ is multiplied on the right by (c), the product $(a) \cdot (b) \cdot (c)$ is associative in the sense that we can conceive it either in the form $\{(a) \cdot (b)\} \cdot (c)$ or in the form $(a) \cdot \{(b) \cdot (c)\}$. In fact in both cases we find that

(13.7) $$\{(a) \cdot (b) \cdot (c)\}_{ij} = \sum_k \sum_h a_{ik} b_{kh} c_{hj}.$$

Let us note the peculiar way in which the indices follow each other on the right-hand side of (13.6) and (13.7). First comes the first index figuring

146

on the left-hand side, then the dummy indices (i.e. the summation indices) each repeated twice, and finally the last of the left-hand indices.

When the three matrices (a), (b), and (c) are equal, (13.7) defines the symbolic cube $(a)^3$. We define in the same way all other matrix powers of positive integral order.

By convention, we denote $(a)^0$ by (e), which is the unit-matrix

(13.8) $$(e)_{ij} = (e_{ij}) = \begin{cases} 1 & \text{when} \quad i = j \\ 0 & \text{when} \quad i \neq j. \end{cases}$$

Having thus defined the multiplication of a matrix by a scalar, (in 13.3)), the sum of two or more matrices (in (13.4)), and all the non-negative powers of a matrix, we can now define the general concept of a polynomial of a matrix. That is to say, if

(13.9) $$P(x) = b_0 + b_1 x + \cdots + b_n x^n$$

is an ordinary polynomial of the ord nary (scalar) variable x, with the ordinary (scalar) coefficients $b_0, \ldots, b_n$, one can also define the polynomial of the square matrix (x) by

(13.10) $$P((x)) = a_0 \cdot (e) + a_1 (x)^1 + a_2 (x)^2 + \cdots + a_n (x)^n$$

It is as well to point out that matrix calculations provide material for a complete algebra. The concept of a polynomial expressed by (13.10) is useful, in particular, when we are looking for numerical methods to determine approximately the values of the greatest and smallest characteristic roots of a matrix. As we have seen, this problem arises if we are searching for sufficient criteria for the extremum of a function of several variables.

Definition of a determinant

We now come to the determinants.

With each square matrix of the form (13.2) we associate a number (in the usual sense of the word) which we call the determinant. We write

(13.11) $$\begin{vmatrix} a_{11} a_{12} \cdots a_{1n} \\ a_{21} a_{22} \cdots a_{2n} \\ \cdot \ \cdot \ \cdot \ \cdot \ \cdot \ \cdot \\ a_{n1} \ a_{n2} \cdots a_{nn} \end{vmatrix}$$

The expression (13.11) which we distinguish by a vertical line on each side of the table of numbers, thus represents a number in the usual sense of the word, namely a determined function of the elements a_{ij}, while the expression (13.2), distinguished by large parentheses, is the symbol of an "entity" (a) for which we can define certain symbolical operations like (13.3), (13.4), etc.

In order to establish how the value of the determinant is derived from its constituent elements, we shall first examine the simplest cases.

Determinants of order one, of order two, of order three

A determinant of order 1 is defined to be equal to the number which is its only element. That is

(13.12) $$|a_{11}| = a_{11}$$

A determinant of order 2 is defined as a cross-product.

(13.13) $$\begin{vmatrix} a_{11} a_{12} \\ a_{21} a_{22} \end{vmatrix} = a_{11}a_{22} - a_{21}a_{12}.$$

The rule is simple: we attach a positive sign to the product of the two elements in the descending diagonal, and a negative sign to the product of the two elements in the ascending diagonal. This is illustrated by

$$\begin{bmatrix} a_{11} & a_{12} \\ a_{21} & a_{22} \end{bmatrix}$$

A determinant of order 3 is defined by

(13.14) $$\begin{vmatrix} a_{11} a_{12} a_{13} \\ a_{21} a_{22} a_{23} \\ a_{31} a_{32} a_{33} \end{vmatrix} = \begin{aligned} &+ (a_{11}a_{22}a_{33} + a_{21}a_{32}a_{13} + a_{31}a_{23}a_{12}) \\ &- (a_{13}a_{22}a_{31} + a_{12}a_{21}a_{33} + a_{11}a_{32}a_{23}) \end{aligned}$$

The products which appear on the right-hand side are obtained easily from the following scheme

(13.15)

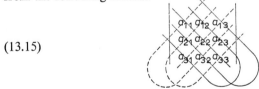

We have here three descending "diagonals" (only the middle one is straight; the other two return in the opposite direction in order that each should include three elements) marked by solid lines. We also have three ascending "diagonals" which are symmetrical to the three descending diagonals. The determinant of order 3 is equal to the sum of three descending diagonals (taken with the + sign) and the three ascending diagonals (taken with the − sign).

The sub-determinants of order two contained in a determinant of order three

To define a determinant of higher order, we shall use a recursive definition, which expresses the value of a determinant of order n with the help of determinants of order $(n-1)$. To do this we first examine the nine sub-determinants of (13.14). These are the determinants of order 2 which are obtained by suppressing one row and one column in the determinant (13.14). Obviously, one can carry out this operation in nine different ways. One can suppress either the first, or the second, or the third row, and in each of these three cases one can suppress either the first, or the second, or the third column. The nine results obtained in this way can be arranged in the form of a new table of three rows and three columns, where the element ij will be the determinant resulting from the suppression in (13.14) of the i-th row and the j-th column. After multiplication by the factor $(-1)^{i+j}$ one obtains the new table (13.16), which we consider, for the moment, simply as a matrix. Thus, for the time being, we shall not take the trouble to calculate the value of its determinant.

$$(13.16) \quad \begin{pmatrix} + \begin{vmatrix} a_{22} a_{23} \\ a_{32} a_{33} \end{vmatrix} & - \begin{vmatrix} a_{21} a_{23} \\ a_{31} a_{33} \end{vmatrix} & + \begin{vmatrix} a_{21} a_{22} \\ a_{31} a_{32} \end{vmatrix} \\ - \begin{vmatrix} a_{12} a_{13} \\ a_{32} a_{33} \end{vmatrix} & + \begin{vmatrix} a_{11} a_{13} \\ a_{31} a_{33} \end{vmatrix} & - \begin{vmatrix} a_{11} a_{12} \\ a_{31} a_{32} \end{vmatrix} \\ + \begin{vmatrix} a_{12} a_{13} \\ a_{22} a_{23} \end{vmatrix} & - \begin{vmatrix} a_{11} a_{13} \\ a_{21} a_{23} \end{vmatrix} & + \begin{vmatrix} a_{11} a_{12} \\ a_{21} a_{22} \end{vmatrix} \end{pmatrix}$$

Let us take as a numerical example, the determinant

$$(13.17) \quad \begin{vmatrix} 3 & 5 & 2 \\ 6 & 9 & 4 \\ 9 & 15 & 7 \end{vmatrix}$$

The sub-determinants – with the signs attached – are:

(13.18)
$$
\begin{pmatrix}
\begin{vmatrix} 9 & 4 \\ 15 & 7 \end{vmatrix} & -\begin{vmatrix} 6 & 4 \\ 9 & 7 \end{vmatrix} & \begin{vmatrix} 6 & 9 \\ 9 & 15 \end{vmatrix} \\
-\begin{vmatrix} 5 & 2 \\ 15 & 7 \end{vmatrix} & \begin{vmatrix} 3 & 2 \\ 9 & 7 \end{vmatrix} & -\begin{vmatrix} 3 & 5 \\ 9 & 15 \end{vmatrix} \\
\begin{vmatrix} 5 & 2 \\ 9 & 4 \end{vmatrix} & -\begin{vmatrix} 3 & 2 \\ 6 & 4 \end{vmatrix} & \begin{vmatrix} 3 & 5 \\ 6 & 9 \end{vmatrix}
\end{pmatrix}
$$

Calculating the value of each determinant of order 2 in (13.18), we have

(13.19)
$$
\begin{pmatrix}
3 & -6 & 9 \\
-5 & 3 & 0 \\
2 & 0 & -3
\end{pmatrix}.
$$

Some remarkable relations

Comparing (13.17) and (13.19) we find the remarkable fact that the sum of the products of any row of (13.17) multiplied by the corresponding row of (13.19) is constant, namely -3. Similarly, the sum of the products of any column of (13.17) multiplied by the corresponding column of (13.19) is also constant, and is also equal to -3. In fact, in the first case, we obtain by taking the first rows: $3 \times 3 + 5 \times (-6) + 2 \times 9 = -3$, and by taking the second rows we obtain: $6 \times (-5) + 9 \times 3 + 4 \times 0 = -3$. Likewise, the sum of the products of the third column of (13.19) multiplied by the third column of (13.17) gives for example: $2 \times 9 + 4 \times 0 + 7 \times (-3) = -3$, etc...

Moreover, if we form the sum of the products of any row of (13.17) multiplied by any other row of (13.19), the result is identically zero. The same is true for the sum of the products of any column of (13.17) multiplied by any other column of (13.19). For example, $3 \times (-5) + 5 \times 3 + 2 \times 0 = 0$; $3 \times 2 + 5 \times 0 + 2 \times (-3) = 0$; $5 \times 3 + 9 \times (-5) + 15 \times 2 = 0$, etc...

This is the expression of a fundamental property of determinants, which we can use if we wish to define the value of the determinant (13.17) of order 3. It turns out that the number -3 given constantly by the above calculations is in fact identical with the value of the determinant (13.17). We can verify this by applying the rule (13.14)–(13.15), which gives: $3 \times 9 \times 7 + 6 \times 15 \times 2 + 9 \times 4 \times 5 - (2 \times 9 \times 9 + 5 \times 6 \times 7 + 3 \times 15 \times 4) = 549 - 552 = -3.$

And we can convince ourselves without trouble that this relation is valid generally, whatever the values a_{ij} in (13.14) and (13.16).

Thus we can define in a simple way the value of the determinant of order 3 by saying that it is obtained by expanding (13.14) along any row, or any column, – "to expand along a row" here means to take the sum of the products of the elements of the given row multiplied by the corresponding sub-determinants, each product being taken with the sign required by the afore-mentioned rule. It is thus possible to define the determinant (13.14) of order three, by means of determinants of order two. Thus we have here a recurrent definition.

This rule is completely general. An elementary line of reasoning permits us to prove that if it is valid for $n-1$, it is also valid for n. Thus we can take as the definition of a determinant of order n the result of its expansion along a row. We will express this precisely by means of a general formula.

Let (a) be a square matrix of order n formed from the elements a_{ij} ($i=1, 2, ..., n; j=1, 2, ..., n$). The value $|a|$ of the determinant of this matrix is given by

(13.20)
$$|a| = \sum_{k=1}^{n} (-1)^{r+k} a_{rk} a_{)rk(} \qquad r = \text{an arbitrary row of } (a)$$

$$|a| = \sum_{k=1}^{n} (-1)^{s+k} a_{ks} a_{)ks(} \qquad s = \text{an arbitrary column of } (a)$$

where $a_{)rk(}$ and $a_{)ks(}$ are the sub-determinants resulting from the suppression of the row indicated by the first index and the column represented by the second index inside the reversed parentheses.

The adjoint elements; fundamental formulae – notably (13.25) – for the expansion of a determinant along a row or a column

The summation indices in the formulae (13.20) do not behave like the indices figuring in (13.6). We realize this by introducing the new symbol

(13.21) $$\hat{a}_{ij} = (-1)^{i+j} a_{)ji(}$$

which is obtained simply, as we see, by transposing (permuting) the rows and columns (and attaching the appropriate signs). The elements $\hat{a}_{ij}$ are called the adjoint elements, and the matrix $(\hat{a})$ constructed from the elements $\hat{a}_{ij}$ is called the adjoint matrix of (a). (See (13.42) concerning the designation of the elements of the transposed adjoint matrix). The formulae (13.20) can now be written as

$$(13.22) \qquad \sum_{1}^{n} a_{rk}\hat{a}_{kr} = \sum_{k=1}^{n} \hat{a}_{sk}a_{ks} = |a|$$

$$r = \text{an arbitrary row of } (a)$$
$$s = \text{an arbitrary column of } (a)$$

(13.22) gives by definition the expansion of the determinant along the r-th row or the s-th column.

$$(13.23) \qquad \sum_{k=1}^{n} a_{rk}\hat{a}_{kR} = \sum_{k=1}^{n} \hat{a}_{sk}a_{kS} = 0$$

$$r \text{ and } R = \text{two arbitrary rows of } (a), \, r \neq R$$
$$s \text{ and } S = \text{two arbitrary columns of } (a), \, s \neq S.$$

Applying the rule (13.6) on the symbolic multiplication of matrices, we see that the formulae (13.22)–(13.23) can be reduced to

$$(13.24) \qquad (a) \cdot (\hat{a}) = (\hat{a}) \cdot (a) = |a| \cdot (e),$$

or, explicitly,

$$(13.25) \qquad \Sigma_k a_{ik}\hat{a}_{kj} = \Sigma_k \hat{a}_{ik}a_{kj} = |a| \cdot e_{ij}$$

$$\text{for } i = 1, 2, \ldots, n \text{ and } j = 1, 2, \ldots, n.$$

The numbers e_{ij} are here equal to 1 if $i = j$ and zero if $i \neq j$. Formula (13.25) turns out to be very useful in the solution of linear equations. We have made use of it in Chapter VIII.

Elementary theorems about determinants

Starting from (13.22)–(13.23), we can obtain without difficulty a series of fundamental theorems concerning determinants.

THEOREM (13.26). When all the elements of a row, or all the elements of a column are zero, the determinant is zero.

One verifies this proposition easily by taking r equal to the index of the row whose elements are all zero, or s equal to the index of the column whose elements are all zero.

Further, one does not change the value of a determinant by adding new rows and columns if the new elements are taken to be 1 in the main diagonal, and to be 0 on one side of this diagonal. The remaining elements can be taken arbitrarily, i.e.

(13.27)
$$
\begin{vmatrix}
1 & \times & \times & \dots & \times & \times & \dots & \times \\
0 & 1 & \times & \dots & & \times & \dots & \times \\
0 & 0 & 1 & \dots & & & & \\
\cdot & \cdot & \cdot & \cdot & \cdot & \cdot & \cdot & \cdot \\
0 & 0 & 0 & \dots & 1 & \times & \times & \times \\
0 & 0 & 0 & \dots & 0 & a_{11} & a_{12} & a_{1n} \\
0 & 0 & 0 & \dots & 0 & a_{21} & a_{22} & a_{2n} \\
\cdot & \cdot & \cdot & \cdot & \cdot & \cdot & \cdot & \cdot \\
0 & 0 & 0 & \dots & 0 & a_{n1} & a_{n2} & a_{nn}
\end{vmatrix}
=
\begin{vmatrix}
a_{11} & a_{12} & \dots & a_{1n} \\
a_{21} & a_{22} & \dots & a_{2n} \\
\cdot & \cdot & & \cdot \\
a_{n1} & a_{n2} & \dots & a_{nn}
\end{vmatrix},
$$

where the crosses × indicate the places where one can put arbitrary elements. In fact, if one expands the left-hand side of (13.27) along the first column, it follows from (13.22) that one obtains 1 times the determinant which is formed by suppressing the first row and the first column. Repeating this operation one obtains the right-hand side of (13.27). The reasoning is completely analogous if we have zeros above the main diagonal and arbitrary numbers below.

THEOREM (13.28). When all the elements of a row or a column are multiplied by the same number, the determinant is multiplied by the same number.

This proposition follows directly from (13.22), since $\hat{a}_{kr}$ is independent of the elements of the r-th row, and $\hat{a}_{sk}$ of the elements of the s-th column.

THEOREM (13.29). The sum of two determinants which differ only in the elements of one row (or one column) is equal to a determinant in which the elements of this row (or column) are equal to the sum of the corresponding elements of the two determinants, while all the other elements are the same as in the two determinants.

For example, let $|a'|$ be a determinant whose r-th row is composed of the elements a'_{rk}, and $|a''|$ a determinant in which the elements of the r-th row are a''_{rk}, all other elements being identical for both determinants. According to (13.22) we have $|a'| = \sum_k a'_{rk} \hat{a}_{kr}$ and $|a''| = \sum_k a''_{rk} \hat{a}_{kr}$, where the $\hat{a}_{kr}$ are the same in both expressions. It follows that $|a'| + |a''| = \sum_k (a'_{rk} + a''_{rk}) \hat{a}_{kr}$. This is the formula for the expression along the r-th row of the determinant whose elements in this row are $(a'_{rk} + a''_{rk})$. (The same reasoning applies to columns).

Generalising (13.29) by means of (13.28), one is led to see that the linear combination of determinants differing only in the elements of a single row is equal to the determinant which results if one applies the same linear combination to the elements of this row. In other words,

$$(13.30) \quad \sum_y w_y \begin{vmatrix} a_{11} & a_{12} & \cdots & a_{1n} \\ \cdot & \cdot & \cdots & \cdot \\ a_{r1.y} & a_{r2.y} & \cdots & a_{rn.y} \\ \cdot & \cdot & \cdots & \cdot \\ a_{n1} & a_{n2} & \cdots & a_{nn} \end{vmatrix} = \begin{vmatrix} a_{11} & a_{12} & \cdots & a_{1n} \\ \cdot & \cdot & \cdots & \cdot \\ \Sigma_\gamma w_\gamma a_{r1.\gamma} & \Sigma_\gamma w_\gamma a_{r2.\gamma} & \cdots & \Sigma_\gamma w_\gamma a_{rn\gamma} \\ \cdot & \cdot & \cdots & \cdot \\ a_{n1} & a_{n2} & \cdots & a_{nn} \end{vmatrix}$$

where w_y are the coefficients and where the summation is done with respect to an arbitrary set of indices. (The formula is analogous for the summation with respect to the elements of a column.)

From (13.22)–(13.23), we deduce directly

THEOREM (13.31). A determinant does not change its value if the elements of a row (column) are increased by the elements of another row (column) multiplied by an arbitrary finite number.

In fact, if we add the elements of the R-th row multiplied by θ to the elements of the r-th row, we obtain a determinant whose expansion along the r-th row is

$$\Sigma_k (a_{rk} + \theta a_{Rk}) \hat{a}_{kr} = \Sigma_k a_{rk} \hat{a}_{kr} + \theta \Sigma_k a_{Rk} \hat{a}_{kr}.$$

The first term of the right-hand side of this formula is equal to $|a|$ by reason of (13.22), and the second term is zero by reason of (13.23), whatever the value of θ. (The reasoning is the same for columns.)

From theorems (13.26) and (13.31) we derive

THEOREM (13.32). A determinant in which two rows (or columns) are proportional is necessarily zero.

In fact, we can take one of the rows and add to it the other row multiplied by the negative of the factor of proportionality between the two rows. In this way we obtain a determinant having a row in which all the elements are zero. (The same reasoning applies to columns.)

This is a generalisation of (13.32)

THEOREM (13.33). Let us consider the numbers $\theta_1, \theta_2, \ldots, \theta_n$ which may be positive or zero, but which are not all simultaneously zero. If

154

between the rows or the columns of the matrix there exists a linear relationship of the form

(13.34)
$$\sum_{k=1}^{n} \theta_k a_{kj} = 0$$

for $j = 1, 2, ..., n$ ($\theta_1, ..., \theta_n$ being independent of j) or

(13.35)
$$\sum_{k=1}^{n} a_{ik}\theta_k = 0$$

for $i = 1, 2, ..., n$ ($\theta_1, ..., \theta_n$ being independent of i) then the determinant $|a|$ is necessarily zero.

In fact, if $\theta_r \neq 0$ (by definition, at least one of the numbers $\theta_1, ..., \theta_n$ is not zero), and we assume the case (13.34), we have

$$-a_{rj} = \frac{\theta_1}{\theta_r}a_{1j} + \frac{\theta_2}{\theta_r}a_{2j} ... \left)\frac{\theta_r}{\theta_r}a_{rj}\right(... + \frac{\theta_n}{\theta_r}a_{nj}$$

for $j = 1, 2, ..., n$

where the term in the reversed parenthesis is omitted.

If we now multiply the first row by θ_1/θ_r, the second row by θ_2/θ_r, etc., and add them all to the r-th row, we obtain a determinant having a row with identically zero elements. In virtue of (13.26), this determinant is necessarily zero.

Arguments based upon (13.33) are very useful in the analysis of certain problems which are capable of being formulated in terms of determinants.

Definition of the rank of a matrix

The idea of a determinant of "order zero" turns out to be useful in the discussion. This concept can be interpreted in a manner analogous to that of 1^0, or of $0!$. In the same way as these two numbers are taken to be equal to 1, we say that

(13.36) $|a| = 1$ when (a) is of zero order.

The concept of the determinant enables us to define the rank of a matrix. The concept of rank is valid for every matrix, and not only for square matrices.

DEFINITION (13.37). We say that the rank of a matrix (square or not) is equal to r, if r is the greatest number having the property that in the matrix there is at least one determinant of order r, which is different from zero. To say that a determinant is "in" the matrix means that we can form it by choosing certain rows and an equal number of columns of the matrix.

It is clear that the rank of a matrix cannot exceed min $[m, n]$, i.e. the smaller of the two numbers m and n. In fact, a matrix of m rows and n columns cannot contain a determinant of higher order than min $[m, n]$.

A square matrix whose rank is equal to its order (i.e. whose determinant is not zero) is said to be nonsingular. On the other hand, if its rank is less than its order, it is said to be singular.

Examples of the calculation of rank

We have an example of a non-singular matrix of order three in the determinant (13.17), which, as we have shown, has the value -3. If we replace in the middle the number 9 by the number 10, we obtain the matrix

$$(13.38) \qquad \begin{pmatrix} 3 & 5 & 2 \\ 6 & 10 & 4 \\ 9 & 15 & 7 \end{pmatrix}$$

We have now a singular matrix of rank 2. In fact, the value of the determinant is zero, which we can easily verify by expanding along the second row and using (13.19). The elements of the second row of (13.19) are independent of the elements of the second row of (13.17), and are thus unaltered by the replacement of 9 by 10 in the middle of the matrix. We have

$$6 \times (-5) + 10 \times 3 + 4 \times 0 = 0.$$

On the other hand, there is in the determinant (13.38) at least one determinant of order 2 which is non-zero. For example, we can take the one situated in the lower right corner, that is $10 \times 7 - 15 \times 4 = 10$. Thus the matrix (13.38) of order 3 is of rank 2.

If we now modify (13.38) by writing 6 instead of 7 in the lower right-hand corner, we obtain the matrix

$$(13.39) \qquad \begin{pmatrix} 3 & 5 & 2 \\ 6 & 10 & 4 \\ 9 & 15 & 6 \end{pmatrix}$$

This matrix is of rank 1, because its three rows are proportional. In fact,

156

the numbers of the second row are twice, and those in the third row are three times those in the first row. Whichever determinant of order 2 we choose in this matrix, the numbers in its two rows will always be proportional. In consequence, in virtue of (13.32), all these determinants will necessarily be zero.

The matrix (13.39) contains at least one (in fact several) determinants of order 1 – simply the elements – which are different from zero. Thus (13.39) is of rank 1.

In the same way we can establish the rank of matrices in which the numbers of rows and columns are unequal.

The inverse of a non-singular square-matrix (a) is denoted by $(a)^{-1}$, and is defined as the adjoint matrix $(\hat{a})$ divided by the scalar $|a|$, i.e. the value of the determinant of the matrix:

$$(13.40) \qquad (a)^{-1} = \frac{(\hat{a})}{|a|}.$$

Thus every matrix has an adjoint, but only non-singular matrices have an inverse.

We have defined above the symbolic non-negative powers of a matrix. Now we can also define $(a)^{-2}$ as $(a)^{-1} \cdot (a^{-1})$, etc. Using this definition of symbolic, negative powers, we can define not only polynomials of the matrix (of the form (13.10)) but also functions of a square matrix which result from a combination of an arbitrary number of integral powers (positive, negative or zero) of the argument.

We can make use of several important formulae concerning the elements of a matrix and its adjoint, which we shall mention here without proof; at most we shall show that they are plausible.

Sylvester's formula for the sub-determinants of the adjoint

$$(13.41) \qquad |\breve{a}|_{pq\ldots r \cdot \alpha\beta\ldots\gamma} = (-1)^N |a|_{)pq\ldots r \cdot \alpha\beta\ldots\gamma(} \cdot |a|^{\nu-1},$$

where $N = p + q + \cdots + r + \alpha + \beta + \cdots + \gamma$, (a) is an arbitrary (singular or non-singular) square matrix, and $|a|$ the value of its determinant. The matrix $(\hat{a})$ is the adjoint of (a), and the matrix $(\breve{a})$ is the matrix as it was before the transposition (permutation of rows and columns) which led to $(\hat{a})$

$$(13.42) \qquad (\breve{a})_{ij} = (-1)^{i+j} a_{)ij(}.$$

In the above numerical examples, $(\breve{a})$ is similar to (13.19) when (a) is (13.17). We can call $(\breve{a})$ the complementary matrix of (a), or the "transpose of the adjoint".

We chose in the complementary matrix $(\breve{a})$ the ν rows distinguished by the indices: p, q, ..., r, and the columns: α, β, ..., γ, then we form the determinant of order ν corresponding to this choice. This is $|\breve{a}|_{pq\ldots r\cdots\alpha\beta\ldots\gamma}$, i.e. the expression on the left-hand side of (13.41). We consider now the determinant obtained by starting from the initial determinant and suppressing the rows and columns corresponding to the above choice of indices. Sylvester's formula says that if we multiply this expression by the $(\nu-1)$st power of the determinant $|a|$, and then multiply the product by the factor $(-1)^{N}$, we obtain the value of the afore-mentioned determinant of order ν.

For $\nu=0$, Sylvester's formula gives $1=1\cdot|a|\cdot|a|^{-1}$, which is trivial. For $\nu=1$, it gives the definition of the elements of the complementary matrix. For greater values of ν, it expresses certain remarkable and very important relations.

Let us take, for example, (13.17) and its complementary matrix (13.19), and consider the case $\nu=2$. We choose in (13.19) the second order determinant situated in the upper left corner: $3\times3-(-5)\times(-6)=-21$. Here $N=1+2+1+2$, i.e. $(-1)^{N}=+1$.

Further, we find that the part of the initial matrix (13.17) which remains after the suppression of the upper left-hand determinant is simply the determinant of order $1:|7|=7$. We have learned above that $|a|=-3$, and thus $|a|^{\nu-1}=-3$. Consequently, the right-hand side of (13.41) is equal to -21, which is equal to the value of the left-hand side.

Passing to the case $\nu=3$, and expressing the value of the determinant of (13.19), we have $-27-(54-90)=9$. On the other hand, the right-hand side of (13.41) is $+1\cdot|a|^{2}=9$, which agrees with the previous result.

Finally, if we apply Sylvester's formula to the case $\nu=n$, we learn that the value of the determinant of the complementary matrix – which is the same as the determinant of the adjoint – is equal to the $(n-1)$st power of the initial determinant.

Gram's formula

We consider two sequences of n functions of a variable t: $x_{1t}, x_{2t}, \ldots, x_{nt}$

and $y_{1t}, y_{2t}, ..., y_{nt}$. We form the sum of the products of x_{it} with y_{jt} as t varies in a given domain. This gives

(13.43)
$$a_{ij} = \sum_t x_{it} y_{jt},$$

where t varies over the domain considered.

Let us examine the determinant $|a|$ of the elements a_{ij}. It can be proved that one can write

(13.44)
$$\begin{vmatrix} a_{11} a_{12} \cdots a_{1n} \\ a_{21} a_{22} \cdots a_{2n} \\ \cdots \cdots \\ a_{n1} a_{n2} \cdots a_{nn} \end{vmatrix} = \frac{1}{n!} \sum_\alpha \sum_\beta \cdots \sum_\gamma \begin{vmatrix} x_{1\alpha} x_{2\alpha} \cdots x_{n\alpha} \\ x_{1\beta} x_{2\beta} \cdots x_{n\beta} \\ \cdots \cdots \\ x_{1\gamma} x_{2\gamma} \cdots x_{n\gamma} \end{vmatrix} \cdot \begin{vmatrix} y_{1\alpha} y_{2\alpha} \cdots y_{n\alpha} \\ y_{1\beta} y_{2\beta} \cdots y_{n\beta} \\ \cdots \cdots \\ y_{1\gamma} y_{2\gamma} \cdots y_{n\gamma} \end{vmatrix},$$

where $\alpha, \beta, ..., \gamma$ are n indices varying independently of each other, in the same domain in which t varies in (13.43). (13.44) is Gram's formula, from which very important conclusions can be drawn.

In order to suggest (but not to prove) that (13.44) is correct, we take the case $n=2$. We have in this case:

$$\frac{1}{2} \sum_\alpha \sum_\beta \begin{vmatrix} x_{1\alpha} x_{2\alpha} \\ x_{1\beta} x_{2\beta} \end{vmatrix} \cdot \begin{vmatrix} y_{1\alpha} y_{2\alpha} \\ y_{1\beta} y_{2\beta} \end{vmatrix} =$$

$$\frac{1}{2} \sum_\alpha \sum_\beta (x_{1\alpha} y_{1\alpha} x_{2\beta} y_{2\beta} - x_{1\beta} y_{2\beta} x_{2\alpha} y_{1\alpha} - x_{1\alpha} y_{2\alpha} x_{2\beta} y_{1\beta} +$$

$$+ x_{1\beta} y_{1\beta} x_{2\alpha} y_{2\alpha}) = \frac{1}{2}(a_{11}a_{22} - a_{12}a_{21} - a_{12}a_{21} + a_{11}a_{22}) = \begin{vmatrix} a_{11} a_{12} \\ a_{21} a_{22} \end{vmatrix}.$$

When $x_{it} = y_{it}$ for $i = 1, 2, ..., n$, we have the moments of the sequence x_{it}, i.e.

(13.45)
$$m_{ij} = \sum_t x_{it} x_{jt}.$$

For the determinant, formed with the moments, we have thus the expansion

(13.46)
$$|m| = \frac{1}{n!} \sum_\alpha \sum_\beta \cdots \sum_\gamma \begin{vmatrix} x_{1\alpha} x_{2\alpha} \cdots x_{n\alpha} \\ x_{1\beta} x_{2\beta} \cdots x_{n\beta} \\ \cdots \cdots \\ x_{1\gamma} x_{2\gamma} \cdots x_{n\gamma} \end{vmatrix}^2.$$

Of course, a matrix of moments is always symmetrical, in the sense that $m_{ij} = m_{ji}$.

The following theorem is a direct consequence of formula (13.46):

THEOREM (13.47). The determinant of the moments of a set of real functions is always non-negative.

It follows from this that correlation-coefficients between two variables, $r = m_{12}(m_{11}m_{12})^{-\frac{1}{2}}$ are necessarily situated between 0 and 1 (here the moments are taken about the means). In fact, in view of (13.47) we must have

$$\begin{vmatrix} m_{11}m_{12} \\ m_{21}m_{22} \end{vmatrix} \geqslant 0.$$

From (13.46) it also follows that if the variables $x_{1t}, x_{2t}, ..., x_{nt}$ are subject to linear relations in the domain of variation of t, i.e. if there exist n constants $\theta_1, \theta_2, ..., \theta_n$ (independent of t, not identically zero) such that

$$(13.48) \qquad \theta_1 x_{1t} + \theta_2 x_{2t} + \cdots + \theta_n x_{nt} = 0 \quad \text{for all} \quad t,$$

the determinant of the moments of these variables is necessarily zero. In fact, in view of (13.33) the determinants which figure on the right-hand side of (13.46) are zero for every combination $\alpha, \beta, ..., \gamma$.

The converse is equally valid: the matrix of moments cannot be zero unless the variables are linearly dependent in the sense of (13.48). One can derive this conclusion from (13.46), with the help of certain specific theorems of the theory of linear equations.

Hadamard's Theorem

By the norm (or more precisely, quadratic norm) of a row we understand the sum of the squares of the elements of this row.

$$(13.49) \qquad p_i^2 = a_{i1}^2 + a_{i2}^2 + \cdots + a_{in}^2 \qquad (i = 1, 2 ... n).$$

Similarly we have the norm of a column

$$(13.50) \qquad q_j^2 = a_{1j}^2 + a_{2j}^2 + \cdots + a_{nj}^2 \qquad (j = 1, 2 ... n).$$

Here is Hadamard's theorem:

160

THEOREM (13.51). The square of a determinant is at the most equal to the product of the norms of its rows; and at the most equal to the product of the norms of the columns.

Thus

$$|a|^2 \leqslant p_1^2 p_2^2 \dots p_n^2 \quad \text{and} \quad |a|^2 \leqslant q_1^2 q_2^2 \dots q_n^2.$$

Figure (13.52) illustrates Hadamard's theorem for two dimensions.

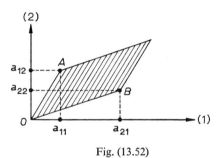

Fig. (13.52)

A and B are two points of a coordinate system constructed on the axes (1) and (2). The coordinates of these two points are, respectively, (a_{11}, a_{12}) for A, and (a_{21}, a_{22}) for B. The area of the shaded parallelogram is

$$\begin{vmatrix} a_{11} a_{12} \\ a_{21} a_{22} \end{vmatrix}.$$

The length of the side OA is $\sqrt{(a_{11}^2 + a_{12}^2)}$, and that of OB is $\sqrt{(a_{21}^2 + a_{22}^2)}$. Clearly, if the lengths OA and OB are given, the greatest area is obtained when OA and OB are perpendicular, in which case this area is equal to the product $OA \cdot OB$. By formulating the theorem for the square of the determinants, we avoid any complications due to the sign of the determinants. Thus we have Hadamard's theorem for $n = 2$.

Theorem concerning the determinant of the product of matrices

THEOREM (13.53). The determinant of a matrix which is the symbolic product of several matrices is equal to the product of the determinants of the matrices which appear in the product.

That is if (a), (b) and (c) are square matrices, one has

$$|(a) \cdot (b) \cdot (c)| = |a| \cdot |b| \cdot |c|.$$

On the left we have the determinant of the symbolic product of matrices; on the right the product of the three scalar numbers, $|a|$, $|b|$, $|c|$. The rule is the same for the product of an arbitrary number of factors.

It is sufficient to prove the case of two factors; since the general theorem can be derived from this by induction.

When the two matrices which are the factors of the product are of order 1 the theorem is obvious.

In the case when the two matrices are of order 2, we have

$$|a| \cdot |b| = \begin{vmatrix} a_{11} a_{12} \\ a_{21} a_{22} \end{vmatrix} \cdot \begin{vmatrix} b_{11} b_{12} \\ b_{21} b_{22} \end{vmatrix} = (a_{11} a_{22} b_{11} b_{22} + a_{21} a_{12} b_{21} b_{12})$$
$$- (a_{21} a_{12} b_{11} b_{22} + a_{11} a_{22} b_{21} b_{12})$$

$$|(a) \cdot (b)| = \begin{vmatrix} (a_{11}b_{11} + a_{12}b_{21})(a_{11}b_{12} + a_{12}b_{22}) \\ (a_{21}b_{11} + a_{22}b_{21})(a_{21}b_{12} + a_{22}b_{22}) \end{vmatrix}$$

$$= (a_{11} a_{22} b_{11} b_{22} + a_{21} a_{12} b_{21} b_{12}) - (a_{21} a_{12} b_{11} b_{22} + a_{11} a_{22} b_{21} b_{12})$$

The right-hand sides of these two relations are equal. Thus the formula of (13.53) is verified for two factors when $n=2$. Manipulating the determinants according to the rules given above, we can prove that the formula is also valid for the product of two matrices of any order. The general theorem (13.53) is thus proved.

Characteristic polynomial of a matrix

The study of the structure of a matrix is greatly facilitated by the knowledge of its characteristic equation.

Let λ be a provisionally arbitrary parameter. The determinant

$$(13.54) \qquad P(\lambda) = \begin{vmatrix} (a_{11} - \lambda) & a_{12} & \cdots & a_{1n} \\ a_{21} & (a_{22} - \lambda) & \cdots & a_{2n} \\ \cdots & \cdots & \cdots & \cdots \\ a_{n1} & a_{n2} & \cdots & (a_{nn} - \lambda) \end{vmatrix}$$

is a polynomial of λ of degree n. This is the characteristic polynomial of the matrix (a) as it was defined by (13.2).

162

We expand this polynomial in powers of λ. This gives

(13.55) $\qquad P(\lambda) = |a| - S_1\lambda + S_2\lambda^2 - \cdots + (-1)^n\lambda^n,$

where

(13.56) $\quad S_k =$ the sum of all the determinants of order $(n-k)$ which can be formed starting from (a) by choosing in all possible ways $(n-k)$ rows, and the columns with the same indices. The number of different choices is $\binom{n}{k}$.

For example, for a matrix of order 2 we obtain:

(13.57) $\qquad P(\lambda) = \begin{vmatrix} a_{11}a_{12} \\ a_{21}a_{22} \end{vmatrix} - (a_{11} + a_{22})\lambda + \lambda^2.$

For a matrix of order 3, we have:

(13.58) $\quad P(\lambda) = \begin{vmatrix} a_{11}a_{12}a_{13} \\ a_{21}a_{22}a_{23} \\ a_{31}a_{32}a_{33} \end{vmatrix} - \left\{ \begin{vmatrix} a_{11}a_{12} \\ a_{21}a_{22} \end{vmatrix} + \begin{vmatrix} a_{11}a_{13} \\ a_{31}a_{33} \end{vmatrix} + \begin{vmatrix} a_{22}a_{23} \\ a_{32}a_{33} \end{vmatrix} \right\}\lambda$

$$+ (a_{11} + a_{22} + a_{33})\lambda^2 - \lambda^3.$$

Similarly for higher orders.

To convince ourselves that the expansion (13.55) is correct, we note that the matrix (13.54) can be written as $(a) - \lambda(e)$. To form the determinant of the sum of two matrices, we can apply, as many times as necessary, the rule (13.29) concerning the sum of two determinants which differ in one column only. Thus we see that the sum of two arbitrary determinants can be written in a "binomial" form, that is, first a term which is the first determinant, then a term which is the sum of n determinants obtained by replacing in every possible way one column of the first matrix by the corresponding column of the second; then a term which is the sum of $\binom{n}{2}$ determinants which can be formed by replacing in all possible ways two columns of the first matrix by the corresponding columns of the second matrix, etc.... The application of this algorithm to the determinant $|(a) - \lambda(e)|$ is given by (13.55).

The fundamental theorem of algebra asserts that a polynomial of degree n has n zeros. Thus we know that the characteristic equation

(13.59) $\qquad\qquad\qquad P(\lambda) = 0$

has n roots (each root being counted as many times as its multiplicity requires).

In the case of a completely arbitrary polynomial, we cannot say in advance whether or not its roots are real or complex. However, in the case of a real symmetrical matrix, the polynomial is of a special composition, which permits us to state the following theorem:

THEOREM (13.60). All the roots of the characteristic equation of a real symmetrical matrix (i.e. a matrix whose elements are real and satisfy $a_{ij} = a_{ji}$) are real.

The proof of this theorem gives a good example of the type of reasoning applicable to the theory of matrices, and it is not particularly arduous. Therefore we give it here in its entirety.*

If $\lambda = \rho$ ($\cos \varphi + i \sin \varphi$) is a zero of the polynomial $\sum_k A_k \lambda^k$ with real coefficients A_k, its complex conjugate $\bar{\lambda} = \rho$ ($\cos \varphi - i \sin \varphi$) is also a zero of this polynomial. In fact, if λ is a root, we must have $\sum_k A_k \rho^k$ ($\cos \varphi k + i \sin \varphi k$) = 0. That is, we have simultaneously:

$$(13.61) \qquad \sum_k A_k \rho^k \cos \varphi k = 0 \quad \text{and} \quad \sum_k A_k \rho^k \sin \varphi k = 0.$$

However, if the two equations (13.61) are satisfied, it is obvious that $\sum_k A_k \rho^k$ ($\cos \varphi k - i \sin \varphi k$) = 0. This means that $\bar{\lambda}$ must be a zero. Applying this result to the characteristic equation (13.59), we see that if λ is a root, $\bar{\lambda}$ must be necessarily another.

Let us assume now that a certain complex number $\lambda = \beta + i\alpha$ is a root, i.e. that for this value of λ the determinant on the right-hand side of (13.54) is zero. Then, according to the theory of homogeneous linear equations, the system

$$(13.62) \qquad \sum_{k=1}^{n} (a_{ik} - \lambda e_{ik}) x_k = 0 \quad \text{for} \quad i = 1, 2, \ldots, n,$$

has a solution in $(x_1, \ldots, x_n)$ where the numbers $x_1, \ldots, x_n$ are not all identically zero. These numbers will be determined with a certain degree of freedom, depending on the rank of the matrix $(a_{ik} - \lambda e_{ik})$; this, however, is of no importance for the present argument. It is sufficient to know

---

* This proof assumes that the reader is familiar with certain properties of complex numbers. These are outlined in the appendix which follows Chapter XIII.

that there exists a solution in $(x_1, ..., x_n)$ where the numbers $x_1, ..., x_n$ are not all identically zero. Since we are assuming for the present that λ could be complex, we have to face the fact that the solution $(x_1, ..., x_n)$ could also be complex. Thus we write

$$(13.63) \qquad x_k = \beta_k + i\alpha_k \qquad\qquad (k = 1, 2, ..., n).$$

Substituting into (13.62), we obtain

$$(13.64) \qquad \sum_{k=1}^{n} [a_{hk} - (\beta + i\alpha)e_{hk}](\beta_k + i\alpha_k) = 0 \quad (h = 1, 2, ..., n).$$

(We now avoid employing i as an index to avoid any confusion with the symbol i representing the imaginary operator.)

Developing (13.64) and separating the real and imaginary parts we find that (13.64) is equivalent to the real equations:

$$(13.65) \qquad \sum_{k=1}^{n} [a_{hk}\beta_k - (\beta\beta_k - \alpha\alpha_k)e_{hk}] = 0.$$

$$(13.66) \qquad \sum_{k=1}^{n} [a_{hk}\alpha_k - (\beta\alpha_k + \alpha\beta_k)e_{hk}] = 0.$$

These equations are not modified if we replace α by $(-\alpha)$ and at the same time replace α_k by $(-\alpha_k)$ for $k = 1, 2, ..., n$. In other words, if $(x_1, ..., x_n)$ is a solution of the linear system (14.62) for λ, $(\bar{x}_1, ..., \bar{x}_n)$ is necessarily a solution for $\bar{\lambda}$. It follows that

$$(13.67) \qquad \sum_{k=1}^{n} (a_{ik} - \bar{\lambda}e_{ik})\bar{x}_k = 0.$$

Multiplying (13.62) by $\bar{x}_h$ and (13.67) by x_h, and summing with respect to h, when we use h instead of i as summation index we obtain

$$(13.68) \qquad \sum_{h=1}^{n} \sum_{k=1}^{n} (a_{hk} - \lambda e_{hk})x_k\bar{x}_h = 0.$$

$$(13.69) \qquad \sum_{h=1}^{n} \sum_{k=1}^{n} (a_{hk} - \bar{\lambda}e_{hk})\bar{x}_k x_h = 0.$$

If in the second of these equations we interchange the summation indices h and k, we obtain

$$(13.70) \qquad \sum_{h=1}^{n} \sum_{k=1}^{n} (a_{kh} - \bar{\lambda}e_{kh})x_k\bar{x}_h = 0.$$

Taking the difference between (13.68) and (13.70), we have

$$(13.71) \qquad (\lambda - \bar{\lambda}) \sum_{h=1}^{n} x_h \bar{x}_h = \sum_{h=1}^{n} \sum_{k=1}^{n} (a_{hk} - a_{kh}) x_k \bar{x}_h.$$

If the matrix a_{hk} is symmetrical, the right-hand side of (13.71) vanishes. Since $x_h \bar{x}_h = \beta_h^2 + \alpha_h^2$ and $\lambda - \bar{\lambda} = 2i\alpha$, in the symmetrical case (13.71) reduces to

$$(13.72) \qquad 2i\alpha \sum_{h=1}^{n} (\beta_h^2 + \alpha_h^2) = 0.$$

(when the matrix (a) is real and symmetrical). Since we have started from a solution $(x_1, \ldots, x_n)$ of the linear system (13.62) where the numbers $x_1, \ldots, x_n$ were not all identically zero, the sum appearing in (13.72) must be strictly positive. That is, (13.72) can be satisfied only if $\alpha = 0$. Consequently, all the roots of the characteristic equation (13.59) are necessarily real.

Let us give the example of a matrix m of order two. The characteristic polynomial is of the form (13.57). The two roots are

$$(13.73) \qquad \lambda = \tfrac{1}{2} \left[a_{11} + a_{22} \pm \sqrt{(a_{11} - a_{22})^2 + 4a_{12}a_{21}} \right].$$

The expression under the root is never negative if the matrix is real and symmetrical, i.e. if $a_{12} = a_{21}$. Consequently, the characteristic equation in the case $n = 2$ never has complex roots.

The fact that the roots of the characteristic equation of a symmetric matrix are real is very important. We have referred to this indirectly in Chapter X, when we discussed the extrema of quadratic forms.

The absolute minimum of necessary knowledge about matrices and determinants

The reader who wishes to limit his study of matrices and determinants to the absolute minimum which is required in applying these concepts, for example, to the theory of linear equations, can content himself with:

(1) Reading from the beginning of Chapter XIII to the end of the paragraph following (13.2); this will provide the general definition of a matrix;

(2) Reading from the paragraph preceding (13.11) to the end of the paragraph preceding (13.20); from this he will learn how to calculate the value of a determinant of any order by a completely elementary method;

(3) Reading from the paragraph which introduces (13.37) to the end of third paragraph following (13.39); this will provide a definition of the concept of the rank of a matrix – a concept especially important for the general discussion of linear equations.

EXAMPLES

EXAMPLE (13.1′).

A natural introduction to the product of two matrices is provided by a very general problem which we will discuss in the case of four variables. (We shall restrict ourselves to square matrices to remain within the meaning of the text, but it will be clear that this restriction is not essential.) This problem is the following: Given four variables x, y, z, u, one wishes to introduce four new variables x_1, y_1, z_1, u_1, by means of a homogeneous linear transformation T_1:

$$T_1 \begin{cases} x_1 = ax + by + cz + du \\ y_1 = a'x + b'y + c'z + d'u \\ z_1 = a''x + b''y + c''z + d''u \\ u_1 = a'''x + b'''y + c'''z + d'''u \end{cases}$$

T_1 is characterised by the matrix

$$\begin{Vmatrix} a & b & c & d \\ a' & b' & c' & d' \\ a'' & b'' & c'' & d'' \\ a''' & b''' & c''' & d''' \end{Vmatrix}$$

A second homogeneous linear transformation T_2 replaces x_1, y_1, z_1, u_1 by the four variables x_2, y_2, z_2, u_2, according to the formulae

$$T_2 \begin{cases} x_2 = \alpha x_1 + \beta y_1 + \gamma z_1 + \delta u_1 \\ y_2 = \alpha' x_1 + \beta' y_1 + \gamma' z_1 + \delta' u_1 \\ z_2 = \alpha'' x_1 + \beta'' y_1 + \gamma'' z_1 + \delta'' u_1 \\ u_2 = \alpha''' x_1 + \beta''' y_1 + \gamma''' z_1 + \delta''' u_1 \end{cases}$$

T_2 is characterised by the matrix

$$\begin{Vmatrix} \alpha & \beta & \gamma & \delta \\ \alpha' & \beta' & \gamma' & \delta' \\ \alpha'' & \beta'' & \gamma'' & \delta'' \\ \alpha''' & \beta''' & \gamma''' & \delta''' \end{Vmatrix}$$

In a very large number of problems it is useful to find a way to pass directly from the initial variables x, y, z, u, to the final variables x_2, y_2, z_2, u_2, by means of a single linear transformation T.

Clearly, one achieves this by substituting into T_2 the values of x_1, y_1, z_1, u_1 derived from T_1. For example, we can represent z_2 by substituting respectively for x_1, y_1, z_1 and u_1 the corresponding expressions containing x_1, y_1, z_1 and u_1:

$$z_2 = \alpha'' \,[ax \quad + by \quad + cz \quad + du \;]$$
$$+ \beta'' \,[a'x \quad + b'y \quad + c'z \quad + d'u\,]$$
$$+ \gamma'' \,[a''x \quad + b''y \quad + c''z + d''u]$$
$$+ \delta'' \,[a'''x + b'''y + c'''z + d'''u]$$

We see now that to find in the expression of z_2 the coefficients of x, y, z, u, one has to take in each case the coefficients of the row of z_2 (i.e. α'', β'', γ'', δ'') and multiply respectively by the coefficients of x, y, z, u in T_1, i.e. by the respective columns of the matrix of T_1.

Now T is the result of the action of transformation T_2 upon T_1, i.e. $T = T_2(T_1)$. In view of the above discussion, we see that the matrix corresponding to T is precisely equal to the product of the two matrices T_2 and T_1 (in this order). Thus, the definition of the product of two matrices (or several matrices) is in fact suggested by the study of such transformations.

EXAMPLE (13.2′).

Let us calculate the value of the determinant D:

$$D = \begin{vmatrix} 1 & 2 & 3 & -4 \\ 3 & 4 & -1 & 2 \\ 2 & -4 & 3 & 1 \\ -3 & 1 & 2 & 4 \end{vmatrix}$$

We shall apply two methods: (1) using the expansion along a row and (2) using theorem 13.31.

1. *Expansion along a row (or column)*

We expand along the second row.
The element of the first column in the second row is 3.
The corresponding adjoint determinant is

$$\begin{vmatrix} 2 & 3 & -4 \\ -4 & 3 & 1 \\ 1 & 2 & 4 \end{vmatrix}$$

The sign of this term is $(-1)^{2+1} = -1$, the exponent $2 + 1$ being the sum of the indices of the row and the column of the element 3.

The element in the second column is 4. Its adjoint determinant is

$$\begin{vmatrix} 1 & 3 & -4 \\ 2 & 3 & 1 \\ -3 & 2 & 4 \end{vmatrix}$$

The sign attached to their product is evidently the opposite to the sign of the first term of the expansion, since in the exponent of (-1) the index of the row is unchanged and the index of the column is increased by one.

168

The first two terms of the expansion are thus:

$$-3\begin{vmatrix} 2 & 3 & -4 \\ -4 & 3 & 1 \\ 1 & 2 & 4 \end{vmatrix} + 4\begin{vmatrix} 1 & 3 & -4 \\ 2 & 3 & 1 \\ -3 & 2 & 4 \end{vmatrix}$$

It is clear that it is sufficient now to alternate the sign of the products starting from the first one, whose sign is determined directly. (It is clear that this sign will be in general $+$ in the case of a row of odd index, and $-$ in the case of an even index.) This gives automatically the expansion

$$D = -3\begin{vmatrix} 2 & 3 & -4 \\ -4 & 3 & 1 \\ 1 & 2 & 4 \end{vmatrix} + 4\begin{vmatrix} 1 & 3 & -4 \\ 2 & 3 & 1 \\ -3 & 2 & 4 \end{vmatrix}$$

$$-(-1)\begin{vmatrix} 1 & 2 & -4 \\ 2 & -4 & 1 \\ -3 & 1 & 4 \end{vmatrix} + 2\begin{vmatrix} 1 & 2 & 3 \\ 2 & -4 & 3 \\ -3 & 1 & 2 \end{vmatrix}$$

If we now expand each determinant of order 3 according to the direct rule, by carrying out the multiplications in succession (which is in general the most practical in numerical examples), we get

$$\begin{aligned} D = & -3\,[24 + 32 + 3 + 12 - 4 + 48] \\ & + 4\,[12 - 16 - 9 - 36 - 2 - 24] \\ & + 1\,[-16 - 8 - 6 + 48 - 1 - 16] \\ & + 2\,[-8 + 6 - 18 - 36 - 8 - 3] \end{aligned}$$

$$\begin{aligned} D &= -3\cdot 115 + 4\,(-75) + 1\,(1) + 2\,(-67) \\ &= -345 - 300 + 1 - 134 = -778 \end{aligned}$$

2. Method of theorem (13.31)

We will use this theorem to make the elements of one row (or column) of D successively equal to zero (except one, in general). For numerical calculations, we can profit from the fact that the first element of D is 1: for example, we shall multiply the first column of D successively by the numbers -2, -3, and 4, (which are the negatives of the elements in the first row), and add these multiples of the first column to the respective columns. In this way all the elements of the first row of the columns (except the first one) will become zero, and this reduces D to the product of its first element with a determinant whose order is one less than that of D. Next we can either continue by this method, or else calculate this determinant of lower order by some other method. Thus we have:

$$D = \begin{vmatrix} 1 & 2+(-2) & 3+(-3) & -4+(4) \\ 3 & 4+(-6) & -1+(-9) & 2+(+12) \\ 2 & -4+(-4) & 3+(-6) & 1+(+8) \\ -3 & 1+(6) & 2+(9) & 4+(-12) \end{vmatrix}$$

$$D = \begin{vmatrix} 1 & 0 & 0 & 0 \\ 3 & -2 & -10 & 14 \\ 2 & -8 & -3 & 9 \\ -3 & 7 & 11 & -8 \end{vmatrix}$$

Thus

$$D = \begin{vmatrix} -2 & -10 & 14 \\ -8 & -3 & 9 \\ 7 & 11 & -8 \end{vmatrix}$$

We continue by multiplying the first column successively by -5 and $+7$, and adding these multiples to the two columns respectively. Omitting the details of the successive additions, we obtain

$$D = \begin{vmatrix} -2 & 0 & 0 \\ -8 & 37 & -47 \\ +7 & -24 & +41 \end{vmatrix}$$

Hence, finally

$$D = -2 \begin{vmatrix} 37 & -47 \\ -24 & +41 \end{vmatrix} = -2\,[(37 \cdot 41) - (24 \cdot 47)]$$

$$D = -2\,(1517 - 1128) = (-2) \times 389$$

$$D = -778.$$

The reader will find at the end of Chapter **VIII** (notably in example (8.1′) (3) further hints on working with determinants.

THEORETICAL APPENDIX ON COMPLEX NUMBERS

We shall now define complex numbers and give a brief account of their most important properties.

We encounter complex numbers when we extract the square root of a negative number. Then we introduce the imaginary operator

(A.1) $$i = \sqrt{-1}.$$

The imaginary operator i is thus a "number" with the property that

(A.2) $$i^2 = -1.$$

A general complex number is a number of the form

(A.3) $$\beta + i\alpha \qquad\qquad i = \sqrt{-1}$$

where β and α are real numbers and i is the imaginary operator.

Two complex numbers are said to be equal if, and only if, they have the same real part and the same imaginary part.

Imaginary part, real part, modulus, argument. Graphical representation

A complex number can be represented graphically as a point A in a plane having a real and an imaginary axis, as indicated in figure (A.4).

The segment going from the origin to the point A is called the radius vector. Its length

(A.5) $$\rho = \sqrt{\beta^2 + \alpha^2}.$$

is called the modulus of the complex number. The modulus is, by definition, a non-negative number. The angle φ formed by the radius vector and the positive real axis – which is counted as positive when it is anti-clockwise – is called the argument of the complex number. Thus we have obviously

(A.6) $$\beta = \rho \cos \varphi \qquad \alpha = \rho \sin \varphi$$

In this way, the complex number can be written as

(A.7) $$\beta + i\alpha = \rho (\cos \varphi + i \sin \varphi).$$

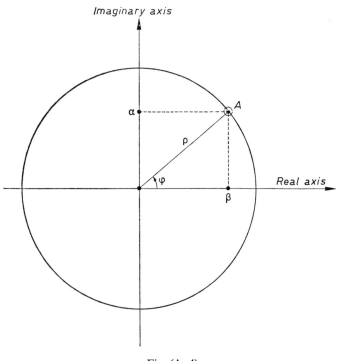

Fig. (A. 4)

For certain operations, it is practical to write the complex number in terms of α and β, in other cases ρ and φ are preferable.

A complex number is zero if and only if its modulus is zero.

The number $\beta - i\alpha$ (the argument thus changing its sign) is called the complex conjugate of $\beta + i\alpha$. When x is an arbitrary complex number, its complex conjugate is denoted by $\bar{x}$. Consequently:

$$\text{real part of } \bar{x} = \text{real part of } x$$

(A.8) and

$$\text{imaginary part of } \bar{x} = -\text{imaginary part of } x$$

The sum and the product of two complex numbers $(\beta' + i\alpha')$ and $(\beta'' + i\alpha'')$ is obtained by ordinary addition and multiplication and by replacing i^2 everywehere by -1. This gives, for example,

(A.9)
$$(\beta' + i\alpha') + (\beta'' + i\alpha'') = (\beta' + \beta'') + i(\alpha' + \alpha'')$$
$$(\beta' + i\alpha') \cdot (\beta'' + i\alpha'') = (\beta'\beta'' - \alpha'\alpha'') + i(\alpha'\beta'' + \beta'\alpha'').$$

Theorem concerning the multiplication of complex numbers

Let ρ and φ be the modulus and the argument of the product of two complex numbers, and ρ', φ' and ρ'', φ'' the corresponding values for the two factors. Then we have

$$\rho^2 = (\beta'\beta'' - \alpha'\alpha'')^2 + (\alpha'\beta'' + \beta'\alpha'')^2$$
$$= (\beta'\beta'')^2 - 2\beta'\beta''\alpha'\alpha'' + (\alpha'\alpha'')^2 + (\alpha'\beta'')^2 + 2\alpha'\beta''\beta'\alpha'' + (\beta'\alpha'')^2$$
$$= (\beta'^2 + \alpha'^2)(\beta''^2 + \alpha''^2).$$

Consequently:

$$\rho = \rho' \cdot \rho''$$

For the argument, we obtain from (A.9) the following relations:

$$\cos \varphi = \beta'\beta'' - \alpha'\alpha'' = \cos \varphi' \cos \varphi'' - \sin \varphi' \sin \varphi'' = \cos(\varphi' + \varphi'')$$
$$\sin \varphi = \alpha'\beta'' + \beta'\alpha'' = \sin \varphi' \cos \varphi'' + \cos \varphi' \sin \varphi'' = \sin(\varphi' + \varphi'')$$

These results can be summed up in the following theorem:

THEOREM (A.10). When two complex numbers are multiplied together, their moduli become multiplied (i.e. $\rho = \rho' \cdot \rho''$) and their arguments become added (i.e. $\varphi = \varphi' + \varphi''$).

BIBLIOGRAPHY

The reader who wishes to acquire a solid knowledge of modern mathematics may read with profit the following books:

APOSTOL, T. M.: *Mathematical Analysis*, Reading, Mass., Addison-Wesley, 1957.
RUDIN, W.: *Principles of Mathematical Analysis*, New York, McGraw-Hill Book Company, Inc., 1953.
SHILOV, G. E.: *An Introduction to the Theory of Linear Spaces*, Englewood Cliffs, N.J., Prentice-Hall, 1961.

The following books were written especially for economists:

ALLEN, R. G. D.: *Mathematical Economics*, London, 1956. (With bibliographic notes.)
TINTNER, G.: *Mathematics and Statistics for Economists*, New York, 1953.
(This work is, in elementary form, a very modern exposition of the diverse mathematical methods whose knowledge is indispensable for those who wish to follow the development of recent mathematical economy.)

These books can be usefully complemented by:

KEMENY, J. G., SNELL, J. L., and THOMPSON, G. L.: *Introduction to Finite Mathematics,* Englewood Cliffs, N.J., Prentice-Hall, 1957. (An accessible work with a minimum of very elementary mathematics.)
KEMENY, J. G., MIRKIL, W. SNELL, J. L., and THOMPSON, G. L.: *Finite Mathematical Structures*, Englewood Cliffs, N. J., Prentice-Hall, 1959.
(Although this book is intended for physicists and engineers, it can be read with profit by economists.)

174

INDEX

Adjoint, cf. Matrix
Approximation 2
Argument 106, 131, (domain of variation)
Argument (of a complex number) 171
Assumptions, basic 3

Bound (lower, upper) 19

Commutative 146; cf. Matrix multiplication from the right; from the left
Conditions; necessary – 3, 22, 27f, 31, 101; concrete example of necessary – 7; sufficient – 3, 23, 101; concrete example of necessary – 7
Continuity (of a function) 3
Cramer's formula 67
Complex numbers 171; graphical representation of – 171; multiplication of – 173

Degree of freedom, cf. Freedom.
Derivative 15ff, 23, *passim*
Determinant; remarkable relations of a – 150; definition of a – 147; expansion of a – 151; diagonal of a – 149; order of –s 148; sub- – 149; elementary theorems of –s 152
Discrete and discrete values, 8
Domain (given in advance) 4.

Equation; characteristic – with 2 variables 109; – with n variables and m conditions) 126.
Equation; linear 6; system of n –s with n unknowns, 66; application of – to economic situations 76f; system of m –s in n unknowns 73; homogeneous systems of –: general theorems, 75

Extremum; problem (definition) of – 4; – of a continuous function 17, 22f; local – 4, 6, 23, 101, 119; global – 4, 5; strong, absolute, weak, relative – 6; search for the simultaneous extrema of several functions 48

Function 9f, *passim*; composite – 48
Freedom; degree of – 12, 68, 85; economic applications of degree of – 95

Gram's formula 158
Graphs; applications to the problem of linear programming 95; finite –, application to economic problems 95

Hadamard's theorem, 160.

Increment; finite – 22
Interval (open, closed) 18f, 127, 134
Imaginary (imaginary part of a complex number) 171

Keynes; model due to – 2

Lagrange multiplier 39, 43, 44, 129
Linear (cf. Equation, Function); – dependence, independence 88, 89; economic applications, 98; – relations between linear equations 92; – relations between functions 91

Matrix; – adjoint 66, 151; – square 144; – definition 144; – multiplication from the right, from the left 146; – notation 144–145; – symbolic operations 146; theorems concerning the product of matrices 146; characteristic polynomial of a – 150; – rank 67f; – calculus 145

175